GW00644836

all Labyrinths

Bettas
Gouramis
Snakeheads
Nandids

Frank Schäfer

Verlag: A.C.S. GmbH, Germany

Inhalt
Contents:

Erklärungen der Abkürzungen in den wissenschaftlichen Namen
Key to the abbreviations in the scientific names

Beispiel/*example*	Belontia signata jonklaasi BENL & TEROFAL, 1975				
	Gattung	Art	Unterart	Erstbeschreiber	Jahr der Erstbeschreibung
	Genus	Species	Subspecies	Author(s)	Year of the description

sp.   = die Art ist bislang nicht bestimmt/*the species is not determined yet*

sp. aff.   = ähnliche Art/*similar species*
Erklärung: Es handelt sich um eine bislang unbestimmte Art, die einer bekannten Art jedoch sehr ähnelt
Explanation: a new species, not determined yet, but very similar to a species already known

cf.   = höchstwahrscheinlich diese Art/*in all probability this species*
Erklärung: Die vorliegenden Exemplare weichen in gewissen Details von der Originalbeschreibung ab, jedoch nicht so gravierend, daß es sich dabei mit einiger Wahrscheinlichkeit um eine andere Art handelt; cf. steht für conferre (lat.) = vergleiche mit
Explanation: the speciemen examined differs in some details from the original description, but not so grave, that is seems (with some probability) to be a different species; cf. stands for the latin word conferre = compare with.

ssp.   = Unterart/*subspecies*
Erklärung: Einige Arten haben ein sehr großes Verbreitungsgebiet; innerhalb dieses Gebietes gibt es Populationen, die sich äußerlich zwar deutlich von anderen Populationen unterscheiden, genetisch jedoch zur gleichen Art gehören. Solchen Populationen erhalten als geografische Unterart einen dritten wissenschaftlichen Namen. Ist die Unterart bislang unbestimmt, so steht hier nur ssp..
Explanation: Some species inhabit an area of very wide range; within this area there are populations that differ optical signifi-cant from other populations, seen in genetic case, they own nevertheless to the same species. Those populations get a third scientific name as geografical subspecies. Is the subspecies not determined yet, on this place only stands ssp..

var.   = Variante/*variation*
Erklärung: Individuelle Abweichungen in der Farbe, die nicht geografisch fixiert werden können, werden als Variant-en bezeichnet. Sie erhalten keine eigene wissenschaftliche Bezeichnung.
Explanation: Individual differences in colour combination, which are not fixed in geografical areas, are so-called variations. They do not get a special scientific name.

Hybride: Mischling zwischen zwei Arten/*crossbreed between two species*
intergrade: gemischte Population zwischen zwei Unterarten/*mixed population between two subspecies*

ERRATUM
- englische Namen, die Personen gewidmet sind, lese man: Brown´s Fighter etc./ *common names, dedicated to persons, have to be written: Brown´s Fighter etc.*
- Kalimantan Barat, Kal. Timur etc. sind Eigennamen und daher groß zu schreiben/ *Kalimantan Barat, Kal. Timur etc. are proper names*
- Anabantoidea, die in CUVIER & VALENCIENNES, 1846 beschrieben sind, sind als VALENCIENNES in CUVIER & VALENCIENNES, 1846 zu zitieren/ *Anabantoidea, described in CUVIER & VALENC have to be cited as follows: VALENCIENNES in CUVIER & VALENCIENNES, 1846*
- das fehlende Zitat auf S. 18 lautet: Belontia signata jonklaasi BENL & TEROFAL, 1975/ *the missing quotation on p. 18 is:* Belontia signata jonklaasi BENL & TEROFAL, 1975
- die korrekte Schreibweise auf S. 56, X40255, lautet: Colisa lalia "RED"/ *the correct spelling on page 56, X40255 is:* Colisa lalia "RED"

all Labyrinths   © **V e r l a g A.C.S. GmbH**

Vorwort

Seit über 20 Jahren beschäftigen mich die Labyrinthfische in Hobby und Beruf. Im Aquarium zählen sie zu meinen bevorzugten Pfleglingen, in der Forschung versuche ich, den Buschfischen ihre Geheimnisse zu entlocken. Doch so intensiv, wie in den letzten 20 Wochen, habe ich mich mit der gesamten Verwandtschaftsgruppe noch nie auseinandergesetzt.

Es ist das erklärte Ziel des Verlages, alle Fische der Erde zu katalogisieren. Das war auch der Anspruch, mit dem an das Labyrintherbuch herangetreten werden mußte. Für den Wissenschaftler in mir Herausforderung und Prüfung zugleich.

Der AQUALOG soll ein Arbeitswerkzeug sein, dessen Benutzer in die Lage versetzt werden, einen lebenden Fisch nach optischen Gesichtspunkten anzusprechen und zu bestimmen. Der AQUALOG kann nicht der Ort für Revisionen oder der Publikation neuer wissenschaftlicher Erkenntnisse sein. Anders ausgedrückt: hier war nicht meine Meinung gefragt, sofern sie im Widerspruch zu bestehenden Lehrmeinungen steht. Wie sollte ich mich nun aber im Falle der Kampffische entscheiden, einer Gattung, in der sowohl in entwicklungsgeschichtlicher, wie auch in systematischer Hinsicht alles im Fluß und ein Ende noch nicht abzusehen ist? Zugunsten sehr vieler Arten oder zugunsten weniger Arten und langer Synonymlisten?

Nach einiger Überlegung und Sichtung des Bildmaterials fiel dann die Entscheidung doch relativ leicht: Der Benutzer, und für den wurde dieses Buch schließlich erstellt, muß in die Lage versetzt werden, sich selbst eine Meinung zu bilden. Auf Synonyme wurde daher fast vollständig verzichtet. In zwei Fällen (Betta channoides und B. rubra) schien es mir auch angezeigt, konservierte Exemplare abzubilden. Ich habe darauf sonst bei den eigentlichen Labyrinthern verzichtet.

Etwas anders gestaltete sich die Entscheidung bei den Nandern und Schlangenköpfen: Hier geistern so viele falsche Zuordnungen durch die Literatur, daß es sinnvoll schien, einmal von Profis bestimmte, konservierte Tiere im Bild zu zeigen.

Zum Schluß noch ein Wort zu den zwei taxonomischen Entscheidungen, die ich dann doch treffen mußte: Die Gattungsnamen Microctenopoma (für die schaumnestbauenden Buschfische) und Parachanna (für die Afrikanischen Schlangenköpfe) habe ich nicht benutzt, da mir eine solche Trennung ohne Untersuchung aller Gattungsangehörigen (einer Revision) nicht sinnvoll erschien.

Ich wünsche allen Lesern, daß ihnen das Buch ein nützliches Werkzeug sein möge und den Labyrinthern, daß sich ihr Freundeskreis vergrößert.

Foreword

For over twenty years, I have indulged myself in the field of Labyrinths as a hobbyist as well as a scientist. In the aquarium, they are my preferred pets, and on the professional level I am trying to gain an insight into the mysterious world of the Bushfish. Still, as intense as for the last twenty weeks, I have never worked on the whole family of Labyrinths.

It is the goal of our publishing company to catalogue all ornamental fish of the world. Logically, it was the goal of AQUALOG-all Labyrinths to catalogue all known fish of the widely spread family of Labyrinths - a difficult task, but also a very tempting one.

The AQUALOG is supposed to be a handy tool for anybody who wants or needs to identify live fish in the aquarium or in nature by exterior characteristics. It cannot be a medium for revisions or the publication of the latest scientific results in the field of Labyrinth research. To put it another way: It is not the medium for publishing my personal opinion when it contradicts the acknowledged scientific teaching. But how was I to decide in the field of the Bettas where everything is still in the making and no definite teaching is available? How should I approach the systematizing - name many species or few species with long synonym lists?

After a lot of thinking and careful examination of the available photographic material the final decision was not too difficult: The user of the book (for whom it is made anyway) must be able to decide for him/herself. Therefore, synonym lists were left almost completely out. In two cases, Betta channoides and B. rubra, I thought it necessary to show pictures of preserved specimens. In the actual Labyrinths, I left this out, too.

A different decision had to be made in the case of Nandids and Snakeheads. Unfortunately, there are so many wrong identifications in the available literature, that is seemed only logical to show preserved specimens that had once been identified by scientists.

Finally, I would like to comment on the two decisions I had to make in using a taxon: I did not use the genus names Microctenopoma (for bubble nesting Bushfish) and Parachanna (for African Snakeheads) because I do not agree with the division of a genus before a careful revision of it has been carried out.

I hope that all readers of this AQUALOG will find it useful and enjoyable, and that the Labyrinths will win even more friends all over the world.

Rodgau, am 19.02.1997

Frank Schäfer

Die Welt der Labyrinthfische

Zunächst einmal: was sind eigentlich Labyrinthfische? Labyrinthfische haben ein Labyrinth. Das haben sie sich schon gedacht? Sie wollen es etwas genauer wissen? Also: ein Labyrinth ist eine kompliziert gebaute Knochenlamelle, die die Fortsetzung des oberen Endes des ersten Kiemenbogens darstellt (Abb.I). Sie liegt in einer Höhle oberhalb des Kiemendeckels (Abb. II). Mit Hilfe dieses Labyrinths können die Fische atmosphärische Luft veratmen.

Die Labyrinthfische gehören zu den barschartigen Fischen, d.h. ihre Rücken- und Afterflosse haben im vorderen Teil geteilte Weichstrahlen, ihre Schwimmblase hat keine Verbindung mehr mit dem Darm. Die Systematik der Labyrinther ist ziemlich kompliziert. Ich will deshalb auch an dieser Stelle gar nicht darauf eingehen, zumal sie die meisten Aquarianer nur am Rande interessiert. In jüngster Zeit beschäftigte sich Ralf BRITZ in seiner Doktorarbeit mit der Systematik der asiatischen Labyrinther (s. Literaturtips). Speziell Interessierte seien auf diese Schrift verwiesen. Über die afrikanischen Labyrinther arbeite ich selbst derzeit, eine umfassende Publikation wird aber erst in ca. drei Jahren zu erwarten sein.

Sieht man mal vom Goldfisch ab, so war es ein Labyrinther, der als erster ausländischer Aquarienfisch eingeführt wurde: *Macropodus opercularis*. In den 60er Jahren des vorigen Jahrhunderts kamen die ersten Exemplare dieser Fische aus China nach Frankreich. Sie waren in einem fürchterlichen Zustand. Und doch gelang es, sie gesund zu pflegen uns zu züchten, eine Leistung, die man gar nicht hoch genug einschätzen kann. Für die ersten Tiere wurden wahnsinnige Preise gezahlt. Die Nüchterneren nannten ihn, in wörtlicher Übersetzung des Gattungsnamens, „Großflosser", doch hatte sich bald ein viel treffenderer Name eingebürgert: „Paradiesfisch", und paradiesisch sieht er auch wirklich aus: tomatenrot der Körper, darauf senkrechte, dunkelblaue Binden, dazu die riesigen, ausgezipfelten Flossen des Männchens: ein Traumfisch. Auch wenn die heutigen Aquarianer, von immer mehr raren Exoten verwöhnt, ihn oft nur noch abwertend „Makropode" nennen, so hat er doch seinen Liebhaberkreis; für viele, so auch für mich, ist der Paradiesfisch immer noch der schönste Aquariumfisch überhaupt. Hier ist nicht der Platz, um auf die vielen faszinierenden Verhaltensweisen dieses Fisches einzugehen, doch lernen wir an seinem Beispiel die „typische" Labyrinthfischbrutpflege kennen: den Schaumnestbau; Das Männchen nimmt von der Wasseroberfläche Luft auf, umhüllt sie mit einem Sekret aus der Maulhöhle und stößt sie in Form von kleinen Bläschen wieder aus. Dank des Sekrets zerplatzen diese Bläschen nicht an der Wasseroberfläche, sondern bleiben erhalten und kleben zusammen, so daß mit der Zeit eine Art Schaumfloß entsteht. Unter diesem Schaumnest wird abge-

laicht, die Eier hineingespuckt und sie und die Larven bis zum Selbständigwerden betreut. Die Schaumnestpflege übernimmt normalerweise das Männchen, das Weibchen verteidigt das weitere Revier.

Diese Verhaltensweise haben viele Labyrinther: die Fadenfische der Gattungen *Trichogaster* und *Colisa* (8 Arten), die beiden weiteren *Macropodus*arten, viele Kampffischarten (*Betta*), die Riesenguramis (*Osphromenus*) und ein Teil der afrikanischen Buschfische (*Ctenopoma*), und zwar die Buschfische, die NORRIS mit dem Gattungsnamen „*Microctenopoma*" belegt hat. Ich folge dieser Auffassung aber vorläufig noch nicht: ohne eine umfassende Gesamtuntersuchung, eine sogenannte Revision, aller Buschfische sind solche Abspaltungen nicht sinnvoll. Während all diese Arten ihr Schaumnest an der Wasseroberfläche zwischen Schwimmpflanzen bauen, ziehen die drei Arten knurrende Guramis (*Trichopsis*) dazu die Blattunterseite großblättriger Wasserpflanzen vor. Eine Weiterentwicklung dieser Verhaltensweise ist das Brüten in Höhlen: die zwei Spitzschwanzmakropoden (*Pseudophromenus cupanus* und *P. dayi*) bauen ihre Schaumnester gerne in kleinen Blumen-

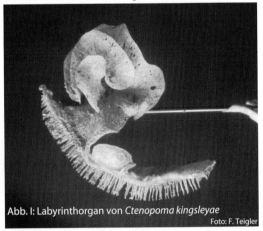

Abb. I: Labyrinthorgan von *Ctenopoma kingsleyae*
Foto: F. Teigler

töpfen, wie auch der Smaragdkampffisch, *Betta smaragdina*. Die *Malpulutta kretseri* von Sri Lanka laicht am liebsten in Bambusstücken, in die sie gerade noch hineinpaßt. Die Prachtzwergguramis der Gattung *Parosphromenus* bauen oft schon gar kein Schaumnest mehr ans Höhlendach: ihre Eier kleben von alleine dort, allerdings nur in weichem Wasser. Die beiden Inselmakropoden der Gattung *Belontia* laichen wieder an der Wasseroberfläche, bauen aber nur ein sehr dürftiges Schaumnest. Alle diese Fische nehmen im Zuge der Brutpflege oft Eier und Jungfische ins Maul, um sie an einen anderen Ort im Nest zu spucken, oder um Ausreißer zurückzubefördern. Darüber hinaus gibt es zwei grobe Einteilungen der Eitypen bei den Labyrinthern: sogenannte Schwimmeier, die durch Öleinlagerungen leichter als Wasser sind und deshalb von alleine schwimmen, und sogenannte Sinkeier, die dotterreicher sind und keinen Auftrieb haben. Der Vorteil der Sinkeier: die Jungfische bekommen mehr Kraftreserven mit auf den Weg ins Leben. Der Nachteil: das pflegende Elterntier muß ständig aufpassen, daß die Eier nicht in den Schlamm sinken und verderben.

© Verlag A.C.S. GmbH

Man kann sich leicht vorstellen, wie daraus Maulbrutpflege entstehen kann. Diese Art von Brutpflege ist dann auch bei vielen Kampffischarten (*Betta*), den Schokoladenguramis (*Sphaerichthys*) und dem Hechtkopf (*Luciocephalus pulcher*) verwirklicht. Üblicherweise pflegen auch hier die Männchen die Eier. Nur beim Schokoladengurami *Sphaerichthys osphromenoides* scheint als der einzigen Labyrinthfischart das Weibchen die Eier im Maul auszubrüten. Die nahe verwandte *S. acrostoma* betreibt dagegen wieder Maulbrutpflege im männlichen Geschlecht. Die dritte *Sphaerichthys*-Art, *S. vaillanti* ist erst kürzlich eingeführt und gezüchtet worden. Sie ist ebenfalls Maulbrüter im männlichen Geschlecht, wie auf dem Foto auf Seite 87 erstmals in der Literatur dokumentiert wird. Leider weiß man noch nichts über das Brutpflegeverhalten von dem in den 80er Jahren in zwei Exemplaren eingeführten *Parasphaerichthys ocellatus*, von dem leider seitdem keine Exemplare mehr bekannt wurden. Hingegen wurde der bis vor wenigen Jahren nahezu unbekannte *Ctenops nobilis* mittlerweile häufiger nachgezüchtet und entpuppte sich als ein weiterer Maulbrüter des Labyrinthergeschlechts.

Abb. II: Labyrinthorgan von *Ctenopoma kingsleyae*; Lage im Schädel
Foto: F. Schäfer

Mit der Umstellung auf die Maulbrutpflege ging auch eine Abwandlung im Ablaichverhalten vor sich: zwar erfolgt vor dem eigentlichen Ablaichen auch hier die U-förmige Umschlingung des Weibchens durch das Männchen, wobei sie auf den Rücken gedreht wird und die Geschlechtsöffnungen sich gegenüberliegen. Dann werden unter dem üblichen heftigen Zittern die Geschlechtsprodukte ausgestoßen, worauf ein charakteristischer Starrezustand beide Partner befällt. Während nun aber bei den Schaumnestbauern das Männchen meist als erstes aus der Starre erwacht und die Eier ins Nest befördert, wobei ihm später das Weibchen hilft, erwacht bei den maulbrütenden Kampffischen (für die anderen Arten siehe die Arbeit von Britz) dagegen das Weibchen zuerst, nimmt die Eier ins Maul und spuckt sie dem Männchen so lange vors Maul, bis es sie alle im Kehlsack untergebracht hat (s. dazu Foto auf Seite 47). Auch später ist die Zusammenarbeit der Beiden intensiver als bei den Schaumnestlern. Das Weibchen verteidigt Männchen und Revier recht nachdrücklich, was sehr sinnvoll ist, denn die Maulbrüterjungen benötigen 10-14 Tage zum Selbstständigwerden, im Gegensatz zu 2-6 Tagen bei den Schaumnestbauern.

Doch treiben nicht alle Labyrinther Brutfürsorge, manche sorgen für die Arterhaltung nur dadurch, daß sie große Mengen von Eiern produzieren. Es sind dies die beiden asiatischen Kletterbarsche (*Anabas*), die über Land wandern können, wenn ihr Wohngewässer austrocknet, wozu sie ihr Labyrinthorgan, die harte Beschuppung und die mit Dornen versehenen Kiemendeckel in die Lage versetzen; dann ein Teil der afrikanischen Buschfische (*Ctenopoma*) und der asiatische Küssende Gurami (*Helostoma temminckii*). Nicht ganz geklärt sind die Verhältnisse bei den Kapbuschfischen der Gattung *Sandelia*.

Es gibt wohl keine andere Verwandschaftsgruppe bei Fischen, die so viele Spezialisierungen und Abwandlungen aufweist, wie die Labyrinther. Vom riesigen Seenbewohner *Osphromenus gorami*, der bis zu 60 cm lang wird, als „Wasserschwein" alles frißt, dazu seinerseits prima schmeckt und in ganz Asien ein wichtiger Marktfisch ist, bis zum gerade mal 2,5 cm langen Prachtzwerggurami, der ein Bewohner von Fallaubschichten in Kleinstgewässern und ein wertvoller, prächtiger Aquarienfisch ist, gibt es viele Übergänge. Die meisten Arten sind wohl Kleintierfresser, wobei Insekten und deren Larven den Hauptanteil stellen. Eine Art, der bereits erwähnte Hechtkopf, ist aber ein spezialisierter Lauerjäger, der sich von kleinen Fischen ernährt. Seine Färbung, zwei dunkelbraune Längsbinden auf ockerfarbigem Grund, und die schlanke Gestalt lassen ihn wie ein treibendes Stöckchen erscheinen, wodurch er sich auf Schnappnähe an die Kleinfische heranschleichen kann. Erstaunlich ist die funktionelle Gleichheit im Kopf- und Körperbau mit unserem einheimischen Hecht *Esox lucius*, was man „Analogie" nennt und zeigt, daß ähnliche Lebensweise ähnliche Anpassungen zur Folge hat.

Das andere Extrem hat der Küssende Gurami entwickelt, dessen Maul mit merkwürdig aufgeworfenen Lippen versehen ist. Er ist ein Filtrierer, der Kleinstlebewesen aus dem Wasser seiht. Das sogenannte „Küssen", das die Tiere häufig praktizieren, ist tatsächlich eine Sonderform des ritualisierten, bei vielen Barschartigen zu beobachtenden Maulzerrens, einer Kampfform, hat also mit dem ritualisierten gegenseitigen Füttern bei uns Menschen nichts zu tun.

In die weitere Verwandtschaft der Labyrinther gehören die afro-asiatischen Schlangenköpfe der Gattung *Channa*. Sie zeigen viele Gemeinsamkeiten mit den Labyrinthern: ein (allerdings anders gebautes) Labyrinth als Hilfsatmungsorgan, was die recht groß werdenden Fische als zählebige Marktfische wichtig macht, und die Brutpflege. Einige, wie *Channa africana*, betreuen als Elternfamilie die Jungfische in einem Pflanzennest an der Wasseroberfläche, andere, wie die relativ kleine (max. 20 cm) und hübsche *Channa orientalis*, sind Maulbrüter. Noch ist nicht allzuviel über die Spezialisierungen im Verhalten der Schlangenkopffische bekannt (für den Vergleich von *Channa orientalis* und *Channa gachua* s. die hervorragende Arbeiten von Ettrich in Aquarienmaganzin 1982, 651-653 und DATZ 7/1986). Ich selbst habe zweimal *Channa gachua* gezüchtet. Dabei stellte sich heraus, daß die Jungfische, die beim Entlassen aus dem Maul bereits ca. 1 cm, lang waren, sich vom Hautsekret beider Eltern ernährten. Von den Eltern isolierte Jungfische starben. Hier ist nicht der Ort und der Platz, um auf diese faszinierenden und praktisch unerforschten Verhaltensweisen der Schlangenkopffische einzugehen. Wir haben ihnen und ihren vielen altersabhängigen Umfärbungen im Bildbestimmungsteil dieses Buches einen breiten Raum eingeräumt, auch in der Hoffnung, die verstärkte Pflege dieser Fische zu forcieren - sie hätten es bestimmt verdient!

Mit Ausnahme der kleinsten Arten (*Channa gachua, orientalis, bleheri* und teilweise auch *stewartii*), die mit Einschränkungen auch in entsprechend eingerichtete und besetzte Gesellschaftsbecken passen, werden die *Channa* durch ihr aggressives Wesen und ihre

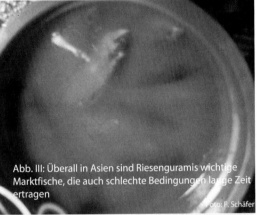

Abb. III: Überall in Asien sind Riesenguramis wichtige Marktfische, die auch schlechte Bedingungen lange Zeit ertragen

Foto: F. Schäfer

Größe meist nur von Spezialisten gepflegt. Das gilt auch, allerdings aus anderen Gründen, für den „Urlabyrinther" *Badis badis*. Der Blaubarsch, mit vier Unterarten in Südasien beheimatet, ist ein kleiner, bis 6 cm langer Höhlenbewohner. Er hat kein Labyrinthorgan, doch aus verschiedenen Gründen stellt man sich die Vorfahren der Labyrinther so vor, wie der Blaubarsch heute noch existiert. Ralf BRITZ kam in seiner Doktorarbeit allerdings zu anderen Ergebnissen. *Badis badis* ist schön gefärbt und zeigt ein interessantes Verhalten (er ist Höhlenbrüter mit Vaterfamilie), nimmt aber nur lebendes Futter und Frostfutter an, weshalb viele Aquarianer seine Pflege scheuen. Der kleine *Badis* wurde lange Zeit zusammen mit der Gattung *Pristolepis* zu den Nanderbarschen gezählt.

Über *Pristolepis* gibt es leider nicht viel zu sagen: kaum jemand pflegt diese Fische und noch weniger Erfahrungsberichte liegen vor. Die wenigen, auf eigenen Erfahrungen beruhenden Berichte zu diesen Fischen lassen sie jedoch als interessante und empfehlenswerte Pfleglinge erscheinen.

Die Nanderbarsche hingegen, mit je zwei Arten in Südamerika und Afrika und drei Arten in Asien verbreitet, haben seit Anbeginn der Aquarienpflege ihre Liebhaber gefunden. Sie zeugen von dem Urkontinent Gondwana, als Südamerika, Indien und Afrika noch eine gemeinsame Landmasse bildeten.

Alle Nanderbarsche benötigen als Ernährungsgrundlage kräftiges Lebendfutter. Am weitesten spezialisiert dabei ist der Blattfisch. Selbst gepflegte Exemplare verschmähten außer Weißen Mückenlarven und kleinen Fischen jegliches andere Futter. Die anderen Arten fressen durchaus auch Bachflohkrebse, Wasserflöhe, andere Mückenlarven etc.. Eingewöhnte Afrikanische Vielstachler (*Polycentropsis abbreviata*) fraßen nach etwa einem halben Jahr auch Frostfutter. Allerdings klappt das nur, wenn die Tiere in Gesellschaft anderer ruhiger Bewohner gehalten werden, die solches Futter bereits gewohnt sind. Man muß sich in diesem Zusammenhang auch von der Vorstellung frei machen, Raubfische (wie es die Nander nun mal sind) seien auch aggressive Fische. Alle Fische, die diesen Tieren nicht als Nahrung dienen, werden gefürchtet oder ignoriert - angegriffen aber nie.

Der bereits erwähnte *Polycentropsis* und die südamerikanischen Arten betreiben Brutpflege. Der afrikanische Vielstachler baut ein Schaumnest (obwohl die Nander mit den Labyrinthern, wissenschaftlich gesehen, nichts zu tun haben). Der Südamerikanische Vielstachler ist Höhlenbrüter und der Blattfisch Offenbrüter. Von den anderen Nandern weiß man nur wenig. Die Asiaten scheinen einerseits keine Brutfürsorge zu üben, andererseits aber auch den Jungfischen nicht nachzustellen.

Ich hoffe, Ihnen mit diesem groben Überblick über eine faszinierende Fischgruppe etwas Appetit auf „mehr" gemacht zu haben. Dieser Appetit kann befriedigt werden!

In diesem AQUALOG werden erstmals alle bekannten Arten, Formen, Varianten und Zuchtformen vorgestellt, sofern Bildmaterial verfügbar war. Ausführliche Berichte zur Pflege und Zucht entnehmen Sie bitte den Zeitschriften und Büchern, die in den „Literaturtips" aufgeführt sind. Überdies haben sich in vielen Teilen der Welt Liebhaber der Labyrinther, Schlangenköpfe und Nander zu Züchtergemeinschaften zusammengeschlossen (siehe Seite 142). Wenden Sie sich an eine der Gemeinschaften, dort erhalten Sie bestimmt weiteres Informationsmaterial zu den Labyrinthern.

Abb. IV: *Macropodus opercularis*; der erste tropische Zierfisch und bis heute einer der schönsten.

Foto: F. Schäfer

© **Verlag A.C.S. GmbH**

The World of Labyrinths

First things first: What kind of fish are Labyrinths? Well, they do have indeed a labyrinth! You thought so yourself? But you would like to have some more detailed information? In this case, you will probably enjoy reading this introduction. A labyrinth is a complicatedly constructed bone lamella which is the extension of the first gill branch's upper end (Fig. I). The lamella lies in a cave above the gill cover (Fig. II). With the help of the 'labyrinth' the fish are able to 'breathe' atmospheric air.

Labyrinths belong to the group of Perciformes, that means, their dorsal and anal fins are devided in a part with hard spiny rays and a part with branched soft rays. Also, the air bladder is no longer connected with the intestines. Systematizing Labyrinths is very complicated. Therefore, I will not deal with this topic in this introduction: most hobbyists are probably only slightly interested in this part of aquaristics. The most recent publication in this field is a PhD thesis by Ralf BRITZ (for further reference, see bibliography) who wrote about the systematology of Asian Labyrinths. I recommend this thesis to anybody who wants to deepen his or her knowledge in this special field. I myself work at the moment on African Labyrinths, but it will take at least three more years before a comprehensive paper will be published.

Except for the Goldfish, a Labyrinth was the first foreign fish imported to European aquariums: Macropodus opercularis. *In the 1860s, the first specimens of this species came to France. They were in a very bad shape, but somehow they were nursed back to health and even successfully bred. This fantastic achievement cannot be praised often enough! For the first animals, incredible prices were paid. Due to its beautiful colour pattern (bright red body with vertical dark blue bands) and the spectacular fan-shaped fins, the fish soon was called 'Paradise Fish' - and a real dream fish it is! Although today's hobbyists are spoiled by the possibility to buy more and more rare exotic species, to me, and to many others, the Paradise Fish is still one of the most beautiful fish I can think of.* Macropodus opercularis *has certainly many, many friends all over the world!*

Unfortunately, it is beyond the bounds of this introduction to go into detail about the fascinating behaviour the fish shows, but the Paradise Fish gives us an idea of the 'typical' brood caring of Labyrinths: the foam nesting. The male takes air at the surface, wraps it in a mouth secretion and releases it in form of small bubbles. Due to the secretion, the bubbles do not burst on the surface but stick together, so that, after a while, a whole 'bubble' (or foam) nest is produced. Under this nest, the fish spawn, then spit the eggs into the nest and later take care of eggs and larvae until the young are independent. The brood caring is usually done by the male, while the female protects the territory.

This behaviour can be observed in many Labyrinths: Gouramis of the genera Trichogaster *and* Colisa *(8 species), the other two* Macropodus *species, many* Betta *species, Giant Gouramis (Osphromenus), and some of the African Bushfish. Here I relate to the Bushfish that* NORRIS *classified as the genus "Microtenopoma". I would like to emphasize that I do not follow this classification until a complete revision of all Bushfish is made and the point of this splitting is proved. All these species build their nests at the surface between waterplants, but the three species of the Croaking Gourami (Trichopsis) prefer the leaf's undersurface of large floating waterplants. The cave brooding is a further development of this breeding technique: the two Spiketailed Paradise Fish species (Pseudophromenus cupanus und P. dayi) like to build their foam nests in small claypots, just like the Smaragd Fighter,* Betta smaragdina. *The*

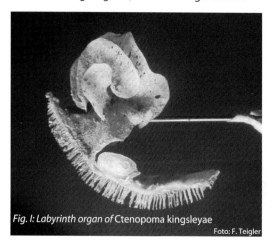

Fig. I: Labyrinth organ of Ctenopoma kingsleyae
Foto: F. Teigler

Malpuluta kretseri *from Sri Lanka prefers to spawn in small pieces of bamboo cane which are just big enough for them to get inside. Very often, the Licorice Gouramis of the genus* Paroshromenus *does not even build foam nests: the eggs stick to the cave ceiling all by themselves, though only in soft water. Both Combtail species of the genus* Belontia *spawn under the water surface, but they only build a very sparse foam nest. During the brood caring, all these fish take eggs or freshly hatched out young into the mouth in order to spit them into the nest or bring back runaways. Also, two types of eggs are distinguished: so-called 'swimming eggs', which are lighter than water because of an oil component and swim by themselves, and the so-called 'sinking eggs' which contain a higher proportion of yolk and therefore lack any buoyancy. The advantage of 'sinking eggs': the fry gets more energy for its way into life; the disadvantage: the caring parent has to watch all the time that the eggs do not sink into the mud on the ground and go bad.*

It is fairly easy to imagine how the mouth brooding technique developed from there on. Consequently, this technique is widely spread among Fighters

(Betta), *Chocalate Gouramis* (Sphaerichthys), *and Pikeheads* (Luciocephalus pulcher). *Usually, also in these species the male takes care of the eggs. The only exception from this rule seems to be the Chocolate Gourami* Sphaerichthys osphronemoides: *in this species, the female seems to be brooding the eggs. The closely related species* Sph. acrostoma *sees the male as brooder. The third* Sphaerichthys *species,* Sph. vaillanti *was imported and bred in France only a little while ago and is also a male-mouth-brooding species, as seen in the photograph on page 87 . In the 80s, two specimens of* Parasphaerichthys ocellatus *were imported to Germany but the fish was not bred, so that there is no information about the brood caring of this species. Since then, unfortunately no other specimens of the species have come to our knowledge, but* Ctenops nobilis *(a completely unknown species until a few years ago) has been successfully bred and proved to be another example of a mouthbrooding Labyrinth.*

Fig. II: Labyrinth organ of Ctenopoma kingsleyae; *position in the skull*   Foto: F. Schäfer

The change to mouthbrooding also caused a change in spawning: It is still performed by the male bending in U-shape around the female which is turned on the back so that the male and the female sex organs are opposite to each other. Then, the sexual products of both animals are expelled under the typical trembling, after which both fish fall into the characteristic paralysis. But now the pattern changes: In the bubble nesters, usually the male first wakes up from this paralyzed state and puts the fertilized eggs into the nest; later, he is joined by the female. In the mouthbrooding Fighters (for Ctenops *and* Luciocephalus *see the PhD thesis by Ralf* Britz *), the females wakes up first, takes the eggs into her mouth and spits them out in front of the male's mouth until he has taken them in completely (see photo on page 47). Also, the further cooperation of the pair is much more intense than in nestbrooding species: The female defends the brooding male and the territory, which is necessary because the fry needs 10-14 days for becoming independent, while the fry of the bubblenesters need only 2-6 days.*

Still, not all species take such intense care of their fry, some only guarantee the survival of the species by producing eggs in high numbers. Like, for example,

*the Asian Climbing Perch (*Anabas*) which can 'wander' across land when its habitat dries up. For this purpose it possesses a labyrinth, hard scales and gill covers protected by thorns. Also, some African Bushfish (*Ctenopoma*) and the Asian Kissing Gourami produce many eggs. The circumstances of brooding in the species of the Capekurpers of the genus* Sandelia *are not yet fully examined.*

There is probably no other family of fish that shows as many behavioural specializations as the Labyrinths. There is the giant lake inhabitant Osphomenus gorami, *that can grow to a length of 60 cm, is known to be an absolute omnivore and is a very popular dish in Asia; and there is the Licorice Gourami, only 2,5 cm long, that lives in leaf covered ponds and is a marvellous aquarium fish; in between, there are countless variations and transitions. Most species probably feed on live food, insects and larvae are certainly the usual prey. The already mentioned Pikehead is one of the more specialized species: It is a predator, feeding on small fish. Its colouration (two vertical dark bands on an ocre body) and its slim features let the Pikehead look like a floating stick. Camouflaged like this, the fish can drift softly near the prey and then quickly catch the surprised victim. A really astonishing fact is the similarity of the head and body features of the Pikehead and the common (native) pike,* Esox lucius. *Similarities like these are called 'analogies'; they show that similar environmental circumstances cause similar adaptions to these circumstances.*

The other extreme on the wide scale of feeding habits is the Kissing Gourami. The strangely turned up lips are used as a means of filtering micro-organisms from the water. The so-called 'kissing' (that can be observed repeatedly) is in fact not a ritualised form of feeding (like in humans) but a special fighting ritual that is performed by many perch-like species.

Another branch of the widely spread family-tree of Labyrinths are the Afro-Asian Snakeheads of the Channa *genus. They show many similarities with Labyrinths: They, too, have a labyrinth (although the Snakeheads' organ is formed differently) as a supporting means of breathing which makes the fairly large growing fish a popular dish, because the fish stays fresh for a long time when it is offered on the market.*
The brood caring is also similar. Some, like the Channa africana, *look after the young in parental care in a plantnest at the watersurface, others, like the very pretty, small (max. 20 cm)* Channa orientalis, *are mouthbrooders. Until today, there is not much information about the behavioural specializations of Snakeheads. For the comparison of* Channa gachua *and* Channa orientalis *see the fabulous works of* Ettrich *in Aquarienmagazin 1982, 651-653 und DATZ 7/1986. I personally succeeded twice in breeding* Channa gachua. *I observed that the fry (that was already ca. 1 cm long when relea-*

sed from the parent's mouth) fed on the parents' body muscus. Young fish, that were isolated from their parents, died. I cannot go into further discussion on this fascinating and literally unexplored fish here, but we hope to raise interest in it. Therefore we included many pictures of the age-depending, different colourations of the Snakeheads - maybe we can convince one or the other reader to try and keep Snakeheads for a change. They really deserve it!

Except for the smaller species (Channa orientalis, gachua, bleheri and stewartii), that can (with reservations) be kept in appropriate community tanks, the Snakeheads are usually kept by specialists due to their size and aggressive behaviour.

Fig. III: All over Asia the Giant Gourami is an important market fish that survives for a long time even worst conditions
Foto: F. Schäfer

This is also true, although for different reasons, for the ancestor of all Labyrinths, Badis badis. The Blue Dwarf and its four subgenera live in Southasia: It is also called Chameleon Fish, grows up to 6 cm length and lives in caves. It doesn't have a labyrinth, but for different reasons the ancestor of the Labyrinths is imagined exactly like the Blue Dwarf in its today's form. (Ralf BRITZ's doctor thesis does not support this idea.) The Blue Dwarf is very pretty coloured and shows an interesting behaviour - it is a cave brooder with male caring. It only takes live and frozen food, a reason for many hobbyists not to keep this worthwhile fish. For a long time, the Blue Dwarf was (together with the genus Pristolepis) ascribed to the family of Nandids. Unfortunately, there is not much to say about Pristolepis: It is rarely kept and even less reported on. But the few informations from keeping the fish recommend it as an interesting and challenging tank inhabitant.

The Nandids, on the other hand, being represented by two species in South America and Africa, and by three species in Asia, were right from the start favourites in the hobby. They are survivors from the ancient continent Godwana, from times when South America, Africa and Asia formed one continent. All Nandids need live food. The most specialized among them is the Leaffish. The specimens I kept only took Glass Mosquito larvae and small fish. Other species also eat Gammarus, Water Fleas and other Mosquito larvae. Well settled African Leaffish (Polycentropsis

abbreviata) also took frozen food after about six months. But they need quiet tank mates that are used to this kind of food. One should remember that predatory fish (like Nandids) are not necessarily aggessive fish - in case of Nandids, all other fish not regarded as food are ignored or even feared - but never attacked.

The already mentioned Polycentropsis and the South American species are brood carers. The African Leaffish build foamnests (although, from a scientific point of view, the Nandids have nothing in common with Labyrinths), the Schomburgk Leaffish is a cave brooder and the Leaffish a ground brooder. About all other Nandids, little information is available. The Asian species seem not to be brood carers, but they neither hunt their fry.

I hope, this rough overview of this fascinating group of fish stimulated some appetite for more! AQUALOG - all Labyrinths tries to satisfy this appetite with showing all known species, variations and breeding forms, as far as photographs were available. For detailed information on caring and breeding, please read the books and magazines listed in the "literature tips" at the end of the book. Also, all over the world, friends of Labyrinths, Snakeheads and Nandids joined together in breeder's associations (please see page142). For more information, please contact one the associations listed.

Fig. IV: Macropodus opercularis; the first and still one of the most beautiful tropical fish.
Foto: F. Schäfer

Bestimmungsschlüssel
für die Gattung *Betta* BLEEKER, 1850 von Kai-Erik Witte

1a Iris des Auges mit irisierenden Flecken (blau oder grün, bei Weibchen etwas blasser): Abb. 1; langgestreckt bis schlank: Abb. 2; Kopf (von oben betrachtet) mit nahezu parallel stehenden Kiemendeckeln: Abb. 3; meist kleiner Kopf (größerer Kopf nur bei der *foerschi*-Arten-gruppe); Maulbrüter (*foerschi*-Artengruppe) oder Schaumnestbauer...- **23**

Abb. 1   Abb. 2   Abb. 3

1b Iris ohne größere irisierende Punkte, einige Arten mit einem dünnen irisierenden Ring um die Pupille: Abb. 4 und 5; schlank bis hochrückig (jedoch Arten *Betta dimidiata*, *B. (schalleri)* sp. F., *B. macrostoma*, *patoti* -*unimaculata* - Artengruppen recht langgestreckt): Abb. 5; Jungfische schlanker als die Alttiere, aber mit , von oben betrachtet, rhombischem Kopf: Abb. 6; Kopf auffallend groß und kräftig; Maulbrüter...- **2**

Abb. 4   Abb. 5   Abb. 6

2a Rückenflosse ungefähr auf Höhe der Mitte der Afterflosse (deutlich hinter den ersten Afterflossenstrahlen); weißer Rand beschränkt auf einen schmalen Streifen am Flossenrand; Gesamtlänge bis 14,3 cm...- **4**

2b Rückenflosse auf Höhe der vorderen Hälfte der Afterflosse (nur wenig hinter den ersten Afterflossenstrahlen); geschlechtsreife Männchen mit breitem weißen Rand an After- und Schwanzflosse; Gesamtlänge bis 5 cm; nur von Borneo bekannt...- **3** (*albimarginata* - Artengruppe)

3a nördliches Kalimantan Timur: Sebuku Flußsystem; ausgewachsene Männchen mit relativ schmalem weißen Rand an After-, Schwanz- und Rückenflosse; Schwanzflosse mit vollständigem weißen Rand und sich daran anschließender dunkler Färbung
Betta (albimarginata) albimarginata KOTTELAT & NG, 1994

3b nördliches Kalimantan Timur: Sesajap Flußsystem; ausgewachsene Männchen mit relativ breitem weißen Rand an After-, Schwanz- und Rückenflosse; Schwanzflosse mit vollständigem weißen Rand und sich daran anschließender dunkler Färbung
Betta (albimarginata) sp. "Malinau (Borneo: Sesajap)"

3c Zentrales Kalimantan Timur: Mahakan Flußsystem; ausgewachsene Männchen mit relativ schmalem weißen Rand an After-, Schwanz- und Rückenflosse; weißer Rand und sich daran anschließende dunkle Färbung erstrecken sich nicht bis zum oberen Teil der Schwanzflosse
Betta (albimarginata) sp. "Pampang (Borneo: Mahakan)"

3d Zentrales Kalimantan Timur: Mahakan Flußsystem; ausgewachsene Männchen unbekannt
Betta (albimarginata) channoides KOTTELAT & NG, 1994

4a Imponieren normalerweise ohne Frontaldrohen (niemals mit weit aufgesperrtem Maul; kleinere Maul: Oberlippe vollständig über Augenhöhe (bei manchen großen Männchen hochrückiger Arten nicht ganz ausgeprägtes Merkmal); gewöhnlich schlank oder hochrückig (jedoch *Betta dimidiata* und *Betta (schalleri)* sp. F langgestreckt); Gesamtlänge bis 14,3 cm...- **7**

4b Imponieren mit Frontaldrohen mit aufgesperrtem Maul; auch ausgewachsenen Fische langgestreckt und mit großem Maul, vor allem die Männchen (Oberlippe erreicht Senkrechte vom vorderen Augenrand): Abb. 7; Gesamtlänge bis 12,5 cm; nur von Borneo bekannt...- **5**

Abb. 7

5a Jungfische und Weibchen normalerweise mit zwei dünnen (etwa: eine Schuppenbreite) und deutlich sichtbaren Streifen und einem Punkt zwischen diesen genau auf der Schwanzwurzel (ein dritter, unterer Längsstreifen ist nur am Kopf vorhanden); dominante Männchen gewöhnlich mit leuchtenden Rottönen (ocker, orange oder rot); ohne blau/grün irisierende Farben am Körper; mit variierenden Querbalken in der gerundeten Schwanzflosse; einige mit Augenfleck in der Rückenflosse; Brunei, nördliches Sarawak
Betta macrostoma REGAN, 1910

5b Körper ohne Zeichnung oder mit Balken oder undeutlichen Streifen: der obere nicht deutlich vom Rückenstreifen abgegrenzt; der mittlere (durch das Auge) endet in einem Fleck auf der Schwanzwurzel (dieser Fleck ist manchmal nicht mit dem Streifen verbunden, befindet sich aber immer in der unteren Hälfte der Schwanzwurzel; mittlerer und unterer Längsstreifen sind am Vorderkörper nicht immer völlig miteinander verschmolzen; Fische in Prachtfärbung (meist Männchen)

in gedecktem Rotbraun, Braun, oder dunkel mit variierendem Anteil von blau/grün irisierenden Glanzschuppen; unpaare Flossen einfarbig, mit mehreren Punktreihen oder gerandet; nie mit Querbalken in der Schwanzflosse oder Augenfleck in der Rückenflosse...- **6**

6a Alle Flossen gerundet wenn gespreizt; in Prachtfärbung mit sehr unterschiedlichen Anteilen von blau/grün irisierenden Glanzschuppen (von nicht vorhanden bis zu den Körper vollständig bedeckend); Kalimantan Tengah, K. Selatan, K. Timur, Sabah...- **8** (*unimaculata* - Artengruppe)

6b Flossen bei ausgewachsenen Tieren spitz ausgezogen, vor allem die Schwanz-flosse der Männchen stark zugespitzt (lanzettförmig): Abb. 8; in Prachtfärbung mit stark unterschiedlichem Anteil von blau/grün irisierenden Glanzschuppen (von nicht vorhanden bis zu Punkten auf fast allen Schuppen); Kalimantan Barat, K. Selatan, K. Timur...- **7** (*patoti* - Artengruppe)

Abb. 8

7a Körper mit vielen (etwas unregelmäßigen) Querstreifen von der Afterflosse bis zur Mitte des Körpers; Flossen ohne auffällige Ränder; Lebendfärbung mit irisierenden Kiemendeckeln; südliches Kalimantan Timur
Betta (patoti) patoti WEBER & DE BEAUFORT, 1922

7b Körper ohne Querstreifen; Lebendfärbung unbekannt; After- und Schwanzflossenränder mit sich anschließendem, auffälligem dunklen Streifen (lebend wahrscheinlich irisierend); Kalimantan Tengah: Barito Flußsystem
Betta (patoti) sp. "oberer Barito (Borneo: Barito)"

7c Körper ohne Querstreifen; Lebendfärbung gedecktes Rotbraun mit blau/grün irisierenden Punkten auf den meisten Körperschuppen; Afterflosse mit dunklem Rand; Kalimantan Barat: Sanggau (Kapuas Flußsystem)
Betta (patoti) sp. "Sanggau (Borneo: Kapuas)"

8a in Prachtfärbung Körper, Kiemendeckel (und Flossen) fast gänzlich mit blau irisierenden Glanzschuppen bedeckt; Kalimantan Timur, Sabah: Tawau, Sandakan
Betta (unimaculata) cf. *unimaculata* POPTA, 1905

8b Lebendfärbung unbekannt; Kalimantan Tengah: Barito Flußsystem
Betta (unimaculata) sp. "oberer Barito (Borneo: Barito)"

8c in Prachtfärbung mit blau irisierenden Kiemendeckeln (nahezu keine auf dem Körper); Unterlippe und Kinn mit bläulich weißen Flecken; Kalimantan Selatan: Pulau Laut
Betta (unimaculata) sp. "Pulau Laut (Borneo)"

8d in Prachtfärbung mit blau irisierenden Glanzschuppen auf den Kiemendeckeln (nahezu keine auf dem Körper); keine weißen Flecke an der Unterlippe (Kinn mit hellen Flächen); Kalimantan Timur: Mahakan Flußsystem
Betta (unimaculata) sp. "Jantur Gemuruh (Borneo: Mahakan)"

8e in Prachtfärbung nahezu ohne blau-metallische Schuppen (einige auf den Kiemendeckeln); keine leuchtend weißen Flecken an der Unterlippe (Kinn mit hellen Flächen); Sabah: Labuk Flußsystem
Betta (unimaculata) sp. "Kampong Gambaron (Borneo: Labuk)"

9a Kopf mit mittlerem Streifen (von Schnauzenspitze durch die Augenmitte) und vollständigem unteren Streifen: Kehlstreifen mit Fortsetzung vom unteren Augenrand bis zur Brustflossenbasis (meist etwas unterbrochen und auf den Kiemendeckeln blasser) : Abb. 5; (bitte hier Weibchen untersuchen, denn ausgewachsene Männchen zeigen häufig nur ein unvollständiges Streifenmuster!); Flossen gerundet oder zugespitzt...- **17**

9b Kopf mit mittlerem Streifen und einige Arten mit einem schrägen Kehlstreifen, jedoch immer ohne Streifen (oder blassen Überrest davon) auf den Kiemendeckeln unterhalb des Auges: Abb. 9 -11; (selten ein oder zwei isolierte schwärzliche Schuppen auf der Kiemendeckelmitte: Abb. 9 -10); Flossen größerer Fische (über 50 mm Gesamtlänge, besonders Männchen) zugespitzt, Schwanzflosse etwas lanzettförmig...- **10**

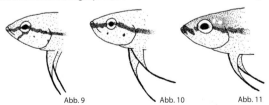

Abb. 9   Abb. 10   Abb. 11

10a Kehlstreifen normalerweise vorhanden (Abb. 9), aber manchmal nicht sichtbar, vor allem bei ausgewachsenen Männchen (z.B. mit Glanzschuppen überdeckt)...- **15**

10b ohne Kehlstreifen: Abb. 11 (bei der schalleri Artengruppe ist manchmal eine dunkle Schuppe unterhalb des Auges zu erkennen und eine oder zwei auf den Kiemendeckeln: Abb. 10; Männchen können so wie oben beschrieben gefärbt sein)...- **11**

11a ohne stark irisierende Kiemendeckel und Alttiere häufig in einer einheitlichen rotbraunen oder sogar schwärzlichen Färbung; die fadenförmigen Bauchflossenstrahlen sind nicht ungewöhnlich verlängert (Abb. 9, 10) und etwas cremefarben; zwei helle Flecke am Kopf hinter den Augen (Abb. 11; manchmal unsichtbar, wenn der Fisch ein-

© Verlag A.C.S. GmbH

farbig ist); Malayische Halbinsel, Sumatra, Kalimantan Barat, K. Tengah, K. Selatan, Sarawak; Gesamtlänge bis 14,3 cm...- **13**

11b ausgewachsene Männchen mit starkem grünlich-blauen Glanz auf den Kiemendeckeln und der Kehle (und hellblauer Körper); Bauchflosse mit sehr langen, leuchtend bläulich-weißen Fadenstrahlen, auffällig vor allem bei größeren Fischen: Abb. 10 (kann bis zur Schwanzwurzel reichen); Kopf ohne helle Flecken; Sumatra, Kalimantan Barat, Sarawak; Gesamtlänge bis zu 12 cm...- **12 (schalleri - Artengruppe)**

12a recht hochrückige Art (Körperhöhe 2,8-3,1 und Kopflänge 2,9-3,1 mal in Standardlänge; Jungtiere schlanker); Sumatra (Jambi), Kalimantan Barat (Kapuas Flußsystem), Sarawak; größere Art, bis zu 11,6 cm lang
Betta (schalleri) sp. E

12b weniger hochrückige Art (Körperhöhe 3,6-3,8 und Kopflänge 2,7-2,9 mal in Standardlänge; Jungtiere schlanker); Banka; kleinere Art, Gesamtlänge mindestens 7 cm
Betta (schalleri) schalleri KOTTELAT & NG, 1994

12c recht langgestreckte Art (Körperhöhe 3,6 und Kopflänge 3,4-3,6 mal in Standardlänge); Verbreitungsgebiet unbekannt; Gesamtlänge bis ca. 9 cm (unzureichend bekannt, da nur zwei Aquarienexemplare ohne FO)
Betta (schalleri) sp. F

12d ähnelt 12 a, jedoch reichen die Bauchflossenstrahlen kaum bis zur zweiten Hälfte der Afterflosse (bei ausgewachsenen Männchen); einige Fische mit Kehlstreifen; Malayische Halbinsel: Johore (& Pahang: Semberong Flußsystem?)
Betta (pugnax) pulchra TAN & TAN, 1996

13a ohne jede Zeichnung auf dem Unterkiefer (oder Kinn) unterhalb der schwarzen Lippen; Abb. 11; mittlerer Streifen zwischen Unterlippe und Auge variabel; Kalimantan Selatan, K. Tengah, K. Barat, Sarawak (?); Gesamtlänge über 12,4 cm
Betta anabatoides BLEEKER, 1851

13b charakteristische Zeichnung auf dem Unterkiefer: Abb. 12 (unterhalb der schwarzen Lippen: variiert von einem breiten Streifen, der sich von der Unterlippe aus nach unten erstreckt, bis zu zwei isolierten Punkten auf dem Kinn); schwarze Oberlippe (speziell bei Alttieren): Abb. 11,12; der mittlere Streifen kann zwischen Auge und Maxillare unterbrochen sein; Malayische Halbinsel (inklusive Pulau Pinang), Sumatra; Gesamtlänge bis zu 14,3 cm...- **14 (waseri - Artengruppe)**

Abb. 12

14a charakteristische Zeichnung unterhalb der schwarzen Lippen: zwei tränenförmige Flecke; Malayische Halbinsel: Pahang
Betta (waseri) waseri KRUMMENACHER, 1986

14b charakteristische Zeichnung unterhalb der schwarzen Lippen: zwei fast parallele senkrechte Streifen; Malayische Halbinsel: Pahang
Betta (waseri) hipposideros NG & KOTTELAT, 1994

14c charakteristische Zeichnung unterhalb der schwarzen Lippen: zwei fast parallele senkrechte Streifen (manchmal an der Unterlippe nicht verschmolzen); Rücken- und Schwanzflossen gewöhnlich einfarbig; Männchen normalerweise mit einem breiten grünen Rand an der Afterflosse; Malayische Halbinsel: Johore, Singapur
Betta (waseri) tomi NG & KOTTELAT, 1994

14d charakteristische Zeichnung unterhalb der schwarzen Lippen: zwei Flecke, die mehr oder weniger zu einem großen Fleck verlaufen; Bintan
Betta (waseri) spilotogena NG & KOTTELAT, 1994

14e charakteristische Zeichnung unterhalb der schwarzen Lippen: nicht ausreichend bekannt; mittleres östliches Sumatra: Siak Flußsystem
Betta (waseri) sp. "Pekanbaru (Sumatra: Siak)"

14f charakteristische Zeichnung auf dem Unterkiefer mit zwei irisierenden grünen Punkten umgeben von einer schwarzen '8' (einschließlich der schwarzen Lippen); Banka
Betta (waseri) chloropharynx KOTTELAT & NG, 1994

15a von Borneo: bitte mit der *akarensis* Artengruppe (einige Fische mit fehlendem unteren Streifen auf den Kiemendeckeln, vor allem bei Jungfischen!) und *Betta dimidiata* vergleichen! ...- **18 & 17b**

15b mit sehr langen Bauchflossenstrahlen (reichen bis hinter die Mitte der Afterflossenbasis bei ausgewachsenen Männchen); bitte mit der *schalleri* Artengruppe vergleichen! ...- **12**

15c keine langen Bauchflossenstrahlen; Borneo, Sumatra, Malayische Halbinsel, Thailand, Kambodscha, Vietnam...- **16 (pugnax - Artengruppe)**

16a Borneo: Kalimantan Timur; Art mit stark irisierenden Farben einschließlich Punkten auf den meisten Körperschuppen (Schuppen oberhalb der Brustflossen nicht irisierend); kleinere Art (?): Gesamtlänge über 8 cm
Betta (pugnax) sp. "Jantur Gemuruh (Borneo: Mahakan)"

16b Borneo: Kalimantan Barat; Männchen mit deutlichen, blauen und schwarzen Streifen oberhalb des Flossensaums der Afterflosse und der

unteren Schwanzflosse; oft dünne oder deutliche Querstreifen auf der Schwanzflosse; kleinere Art (?); Gesamtlänge über 8 cm
Betta (pugnax) enisae KOTTELAT, 1995

16c Sumatra: Gesamtlänge bis zu 13 cm
Betta (pugnax) sp. G

16d östliches Sumatra; kleinere Art: Gesamtlänge bis zu 8 cm
Betta (pugnax) sp. "Bukit Lawang (Sumatra: Bohorok)"

16e weitverbreitet auf der Malayischen Halbinsel (einschließlich Singapur, Pinang, Lankawi, Phuket und Süd-Thailand); Gesamtlänge bis ca. 11 cm
Betta (pugnax) pugnax CANTOR, 1849

16f ähnelt sehr 16e, hat aber einen etwas höheren Körper; ausgewachsene Männchen mit längeren Bauchflossenstrahlen; Körper mit acht Längsreihen großer, irisierender Punkte (im Gegensatz zu weniger Reihen mit kleineren Punkten); Malayische Halbinsel: Johore (& Pahang: Semberong Flußsystem?)
Betta (pugnax) pulchra TAN & TAN, 1996

16g Malayische Halbinsel (offensichtlich nur lokal verbreitet): Tasik Kenyir (Malaysia) und Phatthalung (Thailand); wird oft nicht von 16e unterschieden!; kleinere Art: Gesamtlänge bis zu ca. 7-8 cm
Betta (pugnax) sp. H

16h südöstliches Thailand, Kambodscha, südliches Viet Nam; kleinere Art: Gesamtlänge bis zu etwa 8 cm
Betta (pugnax) prima KOTTELAT, 1994

17a alle Flossen (fast) gerundet (wenn gespreizt): Abb. 5; (mindestens einige der mittleren Strahlen der Schwanzflosse verzweigen schon bei 2 cm, aber Angaben zu *Betta taeniata* fehlen); der untere und der mittlere Streifen verschmelzen gewöhnlich nahe der Schwanzflossenbasis; Schwanzwurzelfleck oft vom Streifen etwas getrennt; Schwanzflosse mit oder ohne halbkreisförmige Querstreifen; Gesamtlänge bis zu 8,2 cm...- **19**

17b Zwergart (Gesamtlänge bis zu 7 cm einschließlich der bis zu 3 cm langen Schwanzflosse!) mit dunklen, z.T. zugespitzten unpaaren Flossen; rotbraun oder stark irisierend (vor allem die Männchen); mittlerer Streifen mit dunklem Seitenfleck (direkt hinter den Brustflossen); Kalimantan Barat: Kapuas Flußsystem
Betta dimidiata ROBERTS, 1989

17c Schwanzflosse (zumindest bei Fischen mit verzweigten Schwanzflossenstrahlen) lanzettförmig (oder mindestens zugespitzt); Verzweigung der Strahlen beginnt erst bei einer Gesamtlänge von über 4 cm; bei einigen Fischen verschmelzen der untere und mittlere Streifen weit vor der Schwanzflossenbasis; viele Männchen mit dunkler, halbkreisförmiger Zeichnung auf der Schwanzflosse: Abb. 8; Gesamtlänge bis zu ca. 14 cm; Borneo, Pulau Natuna Besar...- **18 (akarensis - Artengruppe)**

18a südwestliches Sabah
Betta (akarensis) chini NG, 1993

18b nordöstliches Sarawak
Betta (akarensis) akarensis REGAN, 1910

18c Brunei, Sarawak; Gesamtlänge bis zu etwa 14 cm
Betta (akarensis) climacura VIERKE, 1984

18d Kalimantan Barat, K. Tengah
Betta (akarensis) sp. D

18e Kalimantan Timur
Betta (akarensis) sp. R

18f nördliches Kalimantan Timur, südöstliches Sabah: nahe Tawau
Betta (akarensis) balunga HERRE, 1940

19a mittlerer Streifen oft mit noch dunklerem (und leicht breiteren) Bereich direkt hinter der Brustflossenbasis; heller Zwischenraum zwischen oberem und mittlerem Längsstreifen, der sehr dünn ist (etwa eine halbe Schuppe breit) und daher wirkt wie ein dünner, heller Streifen auf einem dunklen Körper; gestreckte Art; Gesamtlänge bis ca. 5 cm (die Schwanzflosse der Männchen ist gewöhnlich spitz zulaufend); Kalimantan Barat: Kapuas Flußsystem
Betta dimidiata ROBERTS, 1989

19b heller Zwischenraum breiter, etwa eine Schuppe breit; schlanke oder hochrückige Art; Gesamtlänge bis zu 8,2 cm ...- **20**

20a Männchen mit feinen, halbkreisförmigen Querstreifen auf der Schwanzflosse (Weibchen stattdessen Punktreihen) wie auf Abb. 8 (jedoch mit gerundeter Schwanzflosse); bei ausgewachsenen Tieren ist oft ein weiterer, oberer Streifen zu erkennen, was insgesamt vier Längsstreifen ergibt...- **22 (edithae - Artengruppe)**

20b After- und Schwanzflossen der Männchen mit breitem blauen oder schwarzen Rand: Abb. 5; drei Streifen...- **21 (picta - Artengruppe)**

21a südöstliches Thailand, Süd-Kambodscha, südliches Viet Nam; irisierende Flossenränder bei Männchen nicht deutlich begrenzt: vor allem die Schwanzflosse ist fast völlig vom Schimmer bedeckt
Betta (pugnax) prima KOTTELAT, 1994

21b Malayische Halbinsel: südliches Thailand; Farbmuster ähnelt Betta taeniata bei den Männchen (Weibchen mit wenig irisierenden Farben); Gesamtlänge bis zu 6 cm
Betta (picta) simplex KOTTELAT, 1994

21c Borneo: südliches Sarawak; keine Farbunterschiede zwischen Männchen und Weibchen; Flossenränder und Kiemendeckel irisieren in Hellblau; große Art: Gesamtlänge bis etwa 8 cm
Betta (picta) taeniata REGAN, 1910

21d Java, Sumatra (Malayische Halbinsel?); nur die Männchen haben breit gesäumte Flossen in dunklerem irisierenden Blau; Gesamtlänge bis ca. 6 cm
Betta (picta) picta (VALENCIENNES, in CUVIER & VALENCIENNES, 1846)

22a Kehle und auch der hintere Teil der Kiemendeckel schwach durchsichtig; bei brütenden Männchen Eier und Brut deutlich erkennbar; Gesamtlänge bis etwa 5 cm; Sumatra: Jambi
Betta (edithae) sp. "Jambi (Sumatra: Hari)"

22b Kiemenzwischenhäute und Kiemendeckel mehr oder weniger undurchsichtig; Gesamtlänge bis zu 8,2 cm; Borneo, Kalimantan Timur; K. Selatan, K. Tengah, K. Barat, Sumatra: Way Kambas, Malayische Halbinsel (?)
Betta (edithae) edithae VIERKE, 1984 s.l.

23a Schwanzflosse sehr viel länger als der Kopf; Zuchtform von:
Betta (splendens) splendens REGAN, 1910
Betta (splendens) imbellis LADIGES, 1975

23b Schwanzflosse weniger als doppelt so lang wie der Kopf...- **24**

24a kleinere Arten: Gesamtlänge bis zu 7 cm; Schwanzflosse gerundet: Abb. 2, 5 (nur die *foerschi* Artengruppe aus Borneo besitzt manchmal einen verlängerten Strahl, der eine einzelne Verlängerung darstellt, die scharf aus dem Flossenrand hervorsticht)...- **26**

24b große Arten: Gesamtlänge bis zu etwa 11 cm; bei ausgewachsenen und subadulten Tieren ist die Schwanzflosse leicht lanzettförmig mit einigen langen, fadenförmigen Mittelstrahlen: Abb. 13; Malayische Halbinsel, Sumatra, Banka ...- **25** (*bellica* - Artengruppe)

Abb. 13

25a Malayische Halbinsel, nordöstliches Sumatra; bei ausgewachsenen Tieren: Kopf leicht konvex über dem Auge; die Bauchflosse reicht nicht bis zur Mitte der Afterflosse; Gesamtlänge bis zu 11 cm
Betta (bellica) bellica SAUVAGE, 1884

25b mittleres östliches Sumatra, Banka (?); bei ausgewachsenen Tieren: Kopf leicht konkav über dem Auge (was zu einem Buckel am Genick führt); Bauchflossen reichen bis zur Mitte der Afterflosse; Gesamtlänge über 10 cm
Betta (bellica) simorum TAN & TAN, 1996

26a Kopf mit dreieckigem Fleck unterhalb des Auges: Abb. 14; Lebendfärbung unbekannt; Tiefland des nordwestlichen Sumatra (nicht Toba-See!); Gesamtlänge bis zu 5 cm
Betta (splendens) rubra PERUGIA, 1893

Abb. 14

26b Kopf ohne dreieckigen Fleck; unterhalb des Auges nur ein nicht veränderter unterer Streifen (vergl. Abb. 5)...- **27**

27a Kiemenzwischenhaut nur wenig ausgestülpt während des Imponierens (werden die Kiemendeckel gespreizt, so wird die Kiemenhaut nicht speziell zur Schau gestellt); gespreizte Rückenflosse mit fast parallelen Strahlen, erreicht gespreizt nie den Schwanzstiel; Rückenflosse mit schmalem, irisierenden weißen Rand; Körper gestreckt; unpaare Flossen grün/blau irisierend; Flossenstrahlen sowie Membrane sind nur selten durchgängig farbig abgesetzt...- **29**

27b Männchen imponieren (frontal) mit weit abgespreizten Kiemendeckeln und ausgestülpter Kiemenhaut; ausgespreizte Rückenflosse fächerartig, reicht bis zum Schwanzstiel; alle unpaaren Flossen ohne irisierenden Rand; Körper häufig eher hochrückig als gestreckt; rote oder braune Flossenstrahlen unterscheiden sich von den irisierenden Membranen dazwischen, vor allem bei der After- und Schwanzflosse der Männchen...- **28** (*splendens* - Artengruppe)

28a Tiefland des nordwestlichen Sumatra; Kopf mit dreieckigem Fleck unter dem Auge: Abb. 14; Lebendfärbung unbekannt; Gesamtlänge bis zu 5 cm
Betta (splendens) rubra PERUGIA, 1893

28b nordöstliches Sumatra, westliches Borneo (?), Malayische Halbinsel; Kiemendeckel der Männchen gewöhnlich mit Glanzschuppen; Gesamtlänge bis etwa 5 cm
Betta (splendens) imbellis LADIGES, 1975

28c nördliche Malayische Halbinsel, mittleres (und östliches?) Thailand, (entkommene oder ausgesetzte Zuchtformen in ganz Südostasien); Kiemendeckel der Männchen gewöhnlich mit rötlichen Querstreifen; Gesamtlänge bis zu 6 cm
Betta (splendens) splendens REGAN, 1910

28d nördliches bis östliches Thailand, Laos, Kambodscha (mittleres

und unteres Mekong Flußsystem); Kiemendeckel der Männchen mit Glanzschuppen; Gesamtlänge bis zu 7 cm
Betta (splendens) smaragdina LADIGES, 1972

28e unteres Mekong Flußsystem (südliches Viet Nam); Kiemendeckel der Männchen gewöhnlich mit rötlichen Streifen; Gesamtlänge über 5 cm
Betta (splendens) cf. splendens

29a Körper und unpaare Flossen der Männchen sind tiefrot (Körper manchmal gestreift); sind Streifen vorhanden, sind die Glanzschuppen oft reduziert auf einen mehr oder weniger auffallenden Seitenfleck; kleiner Kopf; Kiemendeckel manchmal mit zwei rötlichen (selten gelben) Querstreifen (oft sehr undeutlich); Malayische Halbinsel, Sumatra, Sarawak, Kalimantan Barat, K. Tengah...- **32** (*coccina* - Artengruppe teilweise)

29b Körper und Flossen einheitlich dunkel (manchmal mit einem schwachen Blaustich), zeitweise rote Farbe in den Flossen vorhanden (vor allem in der Bauchflosse); kleiner Kopf; Kiemendeckel nie mit zwei unterscheidbaren Streifen; südliche Malayische Halbinsel, Pulau Bintan ...- **31** (*Betta (coccina) persephone* s.l.)

29c Körper und Flossen einheitlich dunkel (manchmal mit einem blaugrünen Schimmer); Kopf größer, vor allem bei Männchen; Kiemendeckel gewöhnlich mit zwei auffälligen rötlich-gelben Streifen; Borneo, Kalimantan Barat und K. Tengah; Gesamtlänge bis zu 7 cm. ..- **30** (*foerschi* - Artengruppe)

30a Kalimantan Tengah: Kahajan und Sampit Flußsystem
Betta (foerschi) foerschi VIERKE, 1979

30b Kalimantan Tengah, K. Barat: Jelai (-Bila) Flußsystem
Betta (foerschi) strohi SCHALLER & KOTTELAT, 1989

30c Kalimantan Barat: Kapuas Flußsystem und Küstenflußsysteme
Betta (foerschi) cf. strohi

31a Pulau Bintan; leicht gestreckter; Gesamtlänge über 4 cm
Betta (coccina) miniopinna TAN & TAN, 1994

31b südwestliche Malayische Halbinsel; etwas weniger gestreckt; Gesamtlänge bis zu 4,5 cm
Betta (coccina) persephone SCHALLER, 1986

32a ausgezogene Bauchflossenstrahlen leuchtend weiß (manchmal mit blauem Schimmer), die Basis mit demselben Rot wie die anderen Flossenstrahlen oder etwas heller; mit und ohne Seitenfleck ...- **34**

32b ausgezogene Bauchflossenstrahlen schwärzlich, jedoch manchmal mit einem grünlichen Schimmer überzogen, Basis dunkelrot oder schwarz; Männchen gewöhnlich mit leuchtend blau/grün schimmernden Seitenfleck; östliches Sumatra, westliche Malayische Halbinsel ...- **33** (*Betta (coccina) coccina* s.l.)

33a Malayische Halbinsel: Selangor; Irisieren des Körpers ist nicht immer auf den Seitenfleck beschränkt; Seitenfleck manchmal auch bei den Weibchen vorhanden; zweitlängster Bauchflossenstrahl reicht fast bis zur Spitze des ausgezogenen Flossenstrahls; Gesamtlänge über 5 cm
Betta (coccina) livida NG & KOTTELAT, 1992

33b Malayische Halbinsel: Johore (dies könnte ein eigenes Taxon sein!) und östliches Sumatra; Seitenfleck sehr deutlich, Schimmer in der Balz auch auf den umgebenden Schuppen; Weibchen nie mit Seitenfleck; zweitlängster Bauchflossenstrahl deutlich kürzer als der ausgezogene Flossenstrahl: Abb. 2; Gesamtlänge bis zu 5,6 cm
Betta (coccina) coccina VIERKE, 1979

34a gewöhnlich mit Seitenfleck (auch bei den Weibchen) und ohne irisierende Punkte auf den unpaaren Flossen; nordwestliches Borneo: Sarawak; Gesamtlänge bis zu 3,8 cm
Betta (coccina) brownorum WITTE & SCHMIDT, 1992

34b gewöhnlich ohne Seitenfleck; wenn der Fleck erkennbar ist, dann mit weiteren irisierenden Punkten...- **35**

35a ohne irisierende blaugrüne Punkte auf den körpernahen Teilen der unpaaren Flossen; südwestliches Borneo: Kalimantan Barat; Gesamtlänge bis zu 6 cm
Betta (coccina) rutilans WITTE & KOTTELAT, 1991

35b mit blaugrün irisierenden Punkten auf den körpernahen Teilen der unpaaren Flossen; Gesamtlänge bis zu 6 cm...- **36**

36a östliche Malaysische Halbinsel: Pahang; farbiges Streifenmuster während des Imponierens; schwacher oder kein Schimmer auf dem Körper; Gesamtlänge bis zu 6 cm
Betta (coccina) tussyae SCHALLER, 1985

36b Banka; einheitlich rote Grundfarbe mit etwas blaugrünem Schimmer in der Prachtfärbung; Gesamtlänge bis zu 6 cm
Betta (coccina) burdigala KOTTELAT, 1994

36c Kalimantan Tengah; einheitlich rote Grundfarbe mit starkem blaugrünen Schimmer in der Prachtfärbung; Gesamtlänge bis zu 6 cm
Betta (coccina) sp. Pankalanbun

Key to the genus Betta BLEEKER, 1850
by Kai-Erik Witte

1a Iris of the eye with iridescent spots (blue or green, somewhat paler in females): Fig. 1; elongate or slender species: Fig. 2; head with nearly parallel gill covers when viewed from above: Fig. 3; usually small head (bigger in the foerschi - species group); mouth brooders (foerschi - species group) or bubble nesters...- **23**

Fig. 1   Fig. 2   Fig. 3

1b Iris without broad iridescent spots, some with a thin iridescent ring around the pupil (Figs. 4 and 5); slender or stout species (but Betta dimidiata, B. (schalleri) sp. F, B. macrostoma, patoti and unimaculata - species groups quite elongate): Fig. 5 (juveniles generally more slender than adults but even those smaller than 1 cm with rhombic head when viewed from above: Fig. 6); head rather heavy and prominent, usually larger; generally mouth brooders...- **2**

Fig. 4   Fig. 5   Fig. 6

2a Dorsal fin situated approximately over the middle of anal fin (considerably behind the first anal fin rays); white margins restricted to a very narrow stripe along the edge of the fin; total length up to 14.3 cm...- **4**

2b Dorsal fin situated above the anterior half of the anal fin (only slightly behind the first anal fin rays); adult males with broad white margins on anal and caudal fins; total length up to 5 cm; only known from Borneo ...- **3 (albimarginata - species group)**

3a Northern Kalimantan Timur: Sebuku River basin; adult males with relatively narrow white margin in anal, caudal and dorsal fins, caudal with complete white margin and dark submarginal area
Betta (albimarginata) albomarginata KOTTELAT & NG, 1994

3b Northern Kalimantan Timur: Sesajap River basin; adult males with relatively broad white margin in anal, caudal and dorsal fins, caudal with complete white margin and dark submarginal area
Betta (albimarginata) sp. "Malinau (Borneo: Sesajap)"

3c Central Kalimantan Timur: lower Mahakan River basin; adult males with relatively narrow white margin in anal, caudal and dorsal fins; white margin and dark submarginal area do not extend up to dorsal part of caudal fin
Betta (albimarginata) sp. "Pampang (Borneo: Mahakan)"

3d Central Kalimantan Timur: middle Mahakan River basin; adult males unknown
Betta (albimarginata) channoides KOTTELAT & NG, 1994

4a Aggressive behaviour usually without face-to-face threats (never with strongly opened mouth); with smaller mouth: upper lip completely in front of eye (somewhat intermediate in large males of a few stout species); usually slender or stout species (but Betta dimidiata and B. (schalleri) sp. F elongate); total length up to 14.3 cm...- **7**

4b Aggressive behaviour includes face-to-face threatening with opened mouth; even adult fish elongate and with large mouth, especially in males (upper lip reaching vertical from front margin of the eye): Fig. 7; total length up to 12.5 cm; only known from Borneo...- **5**

Fig. 7

5a Juveniles and females usually with two distinct, thin (i.e. one scale wide) stripes and a spot between them on caudal base (a third, lower stripe only present on head); dominant males usually brightly reddish coloured (ochre, orange, or red), without blue/green iridescent colours on body, and variable crossbars in the rounded caudal fin, some with ocellus in dorsal fin; Brunei, northern Sarawak
Betta macrostoma REGAN, 1910

5b Body with no markings, or with bars or indistinct stripes: upper one not clearly separated from the correspondingly coloured back and central one (through the eye) ending in a spot on caudal base (this spot is sometimes separated from the stripe but still in lower half of the caudal base); central and lower stripes may be not fully fused anteriorly; fish in display colouration (usually males) dull reddish brown, brown or dark with variable amount of blue/green iridescent colours; unpaired fins plain, with series of small spots or with submarginal stripes, neither crossbars in caudal, nor ocellus in dorsal fin...- **6**

6a All fins rounded, when spread out; in display colouration with very variable amount of blue/green iridescent scales (from absent to nearly covering the body); Kalimantan Tengah, K. Selatan, K. Timur, Sabah ...- **8 (unimaculata - species group)**

6b Fins in adults pointed, especially caudal of males rhomboid: Fig. 8; in display colouration with very variable amount of blue/green iridescent scales (from absent to spots on most scales); Kalimantan Barat, K. Selatan, K. Timur...- **7 (patoti - species group)**

Fig. 8

7a Body with many (somewhat irregular) bars extending from anal fin to middle of the body; fins without prominent margins; live colouration with iridescent gill covers; southern Kalimantan Timur
Betta (patoti) patoti WEBER & BEAUFORT, 1922

7b No bars on body; live colouration unknown; anal and caudal fin margins with a prominent dark submarginal stripe (in live probably iridescent); Kalimantan Tengah: Barito River basin
Betta (patoti) sp. "Upper Barito (Borneo: Barito)"

7c No bars on body; in live dull reddish brown with blue/green iridescent spots on most lateral scales; anal fin with dark margin; Kalimantan Barat: Sanggau (Kapuas River basin)
Betta (patoti) sp. "Sanggau (Borneo: Kapuas)"

8a Display colouration with body, gill covers (and fins) almost completely covered by iridescent blue; Kalimantan Timur, Sabah: Tawau, Sandakan
Betta (unimaculata) cf. unimaculata (POPTA, 1905)

8b Live colouration unknown; Kalimantan Tengah: Barito River basin
Betta (unimaculata) sp. "Upper Barito (Borneo: Barito)"

8c Display colouration with iridescent blue gill covers (nearly none on body); lower lip and chin with bright bluish white spots; Kalimantan Selatan: Pulau Laut
Betta (unimaculata) sp. "Pulau Laut (Borneo)"

8d Display colouration with iridescent blue gill covers (nearly none on body); no bright white spots on the lower lip (chin with pale areas); Kalimantan Timur: Mahakan River basin
Betta (unimaculata) sp. "Jantur Gemuruh (Borneo: Mahakan)"

8e Display colouration nearly without metallic blue scales (a few on the gill covers); no bright white spots on the lower lip (chin with pale areas); Sabah: Labuk River basin
Betta (unimaculata) sp. "Kampong Gambaron (Borneo: Labuk)"

9a Head with central stripe (from snout tip through center of the eye) and complete lower stripe: stripe to the throat continuing backwards from lower edge of the eye towards pectoral fin base (usually somewhat interrupted and faint on gill cover): Fig. 5 (Check females: adult males usually don't display the complete stripe pattern!); fins rounded or pointed...- **17**

9b Head with central stripe and some species with an oblique 'stripe-to-the-throat' but always without stripe (or faint remainings of it) on gill cover below the eye: Figs. 9 - 11 (seldom one or two isolated blackish scales on middle of gill cover: Figs. 9 - 10); fins of larger fish (more than 50 mm total length, especially males) pointed, caudal somewhat rhomboid...-**10**

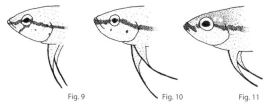

Fig. 9   Fig. 10   Fig. 11

10a Stripe to the throat usually present (Fig. 9) but sometimes not visible, especially in adult males (i.e. covered by bright iridescence)...- **15**

10b Without stripe to the throat: Fig. 11 (in schalleri species group sometimes one darker scale present below the eye and one or two on gill cover: Fig. 10; adult males may be coloured as described above)...- **11**

11a Without bright iridescent gill covers and adults often with uniform reddish brown or even blackish colouration; filamentous pelvic ray not unusually extended (Figs. 9, 10) and somewhat cream coloured; two light spots on head behind eyes (Fig. 11; may be not visible if fish is uniformly coloured), Malay Peninsula, Sumatra, Kalimantan Barat, K. Tengah, K. Selatan, Sarawak; total length up to 14.3 cm...- **13**

11b Adult males with bright greenish-blue iridescence on gill covers and throat (and light blue body); pelvic fin with very long, bright bluish-white filamentous ray, especially prominent in larger fish: Fig. 10 (may reach caudal base); head without light spots on top (see below); Sumatra, Kalimantan Barat, Sarawak; total length up to 12 cm...- **12 (schalleri - species group)**

12a Quite stout species (dorsal depth 2.8-3.1 times and head length 2.9-3-1 times in standard length / juveniles more slender); Sumatra (Jambi), Kalimantan Barat (Kapuas River basin), Sarawak; larger species, total length up to 11.6 cm
Betta (schalleri) sp. E

12b Moderately stout species (dorsal depth 3.6-3.8 times and head length 2.7-2.9 times in standard length / juveniles more slender); Banka; smaller species, total length over 7 cm
Betta (schalleri) schalleri KOTTELAT & NG, 1994

12c Quite elongate species (dorsal depth 3.6 times and head length 3.4-3.6 times in standard length); distribution unknown; total length up to some 9 cm (unsufficiently known from only two aquarium fish)
Betta (schalleri) sp. F

12d Similar to '12a' but filamentous pelvic ray hardly reaching second half of anal fin base (in adult males) and some fish with stripe to the throat; Malay Peninsula: Johore (& Pahang: Semborong River basin?)
Betta (pugnax) pulchra TAN & TAN, 1996

13a Without any dark pattern on the lower jar (or chin) below the black lips; central stripe between lower lip and eye with variable modifications; Fig. 11; Kalimantan Selatan, K. Tengah, K. Barat, Sarawak (?); total length over 12.4 cm
Betta anabatoides BLEEKER, 1851

13b Characteristic dark pattern on lower jar: Fig.12 (below the black lips, there is a diversity from a broad bar extending downwards from the lower lip to two spots lying isolated on the chin); upper lip black (especially in adults): Figs. 11, 12; the central stripe may be interrupted between eye and maxillary; Malay Peninsula (including Pulau Pinang), Sumatra; total length up to 14.3 cm...- **14 (waseri - species group)**

Fig. 12

14a Characteristic pattern below the black lips; two teardrop-shaped spots; Malay Peninsula: Pahang
Betta (waseri) waseri KRUMMENACHER, 1986

14b Characteristic pattern below the black lips: two somewhat parallel vertical stripes extending ventrally; Malay Peninsula: Penang (?), Perak, Selangor
Betta (waseri) hipposideros NG & KOTTELAT, 1994

14c Characteristic pattern below the black lips: two somewhat parallel vertical stripes (sometimes not fused to lower lip); dorsal and caudal fins usually plain; males with a usually broad green margin of anal fin; Malay peninsula: Johore, Singapore
Betta (waseri) tomi NG & KOTTELAT, 1994

14e Characteristic pattern below the black lips: two spots more or less fused into a blotch; Bintan
Betta (waseri) spilotogena NG & KOTTELAT, 1994

14f Characteristic pattern below the black lips: not sufficiently known; central eastern Sumatra: Siak River basin
Betta (waseri) sp. "Pekanbaru (Sumatra: Siak)"

14g Characteristic pattern on the lower jaw with two large, iridescent green spots surrounded by a black '8' (including the black lips); Banka
Betta (waseri) chloropharynx KOTTELAT & NG, 1994

15a From Borneo: compare with akarensis species group (some fish with missing lower stripe on the gill covers, especially in juveniles!) and Betta dimidiata!...- **18 & 17b**

15b With very long pelvic fin ray (reaching beyond the middle of anal fin base in adult males): compare with schalleri species group...- **12**

15c Without very long pelvic fin ray; Borneo, Sumatra, Malay Peninsula, Thailand, Cambodia, Viet Nam...- **16 (pugnax - species group)**

16a Borneo: Kalimantan Timur; species with strongly iridescent colours including spots on most scales on the body (region above the pectoral fin without iridescence); smaller species (?): total length over 8 cm
Betta (pugnax) sp. "Jantur Gemuruh (Borneo: Mahakan)"

16b Borneo: Kalimantan Barat; males with distinct, blue and black sub-marginal stripes in the anal fin and lower caudal; often thin as well as quite strong vertical patterning in the caudal fin; smaller species (?): total length over 8 cm
Betta (pugnax) enisae KOTTELAT, 1995

16c Sumatra: total length up to 13 cm
Betta (pugnax) sp. G

16d Eastern Sumatra; smaller species: total length up to 8 cm
Betta (pugnax) sp. "Bukit Lawang (Sumatra: Bohorok)"

16e Widely distributed on the Malay Peninsula (including Singapore, Pinang,

Lankawi, Phuket, and southern Thailand); total length up to some 11 cm
Betta (pugnax) pugnax CANTOR, 1849

16f Very similar to '16e' but somewhat higher body; adult males with longer filamentous pelvic ray and longer body with 8 longitudinal rows of large iridescent spots (vs usually fewer rows with smaller spots); Malay Peninsula: Johore (& Pahang: Semborong River basin?)
Betta (pugnax) pulchra TAN & TAN, 1996

16g Malay Peninsula (apparently locally distributed only): Tasik Kenyir (Malaysia) and Phatthalung (Thailand) - often not distinguished from '16e'! smaller species: total length up to some 7-8 cm
Betta (pugnax) sp. H

16h Southeastern Thailand, Cambodia, southern Viet Nam; smaller species: total length up to some 8 cm
Betta (pugnax) prima KOTTELAT, 1994

17a All fins (nearly) rounded (when spread out): Fig. 5; (at least some of the central rays of caudal fin already branched at 2 cm total length, but data on Betta taeniata missing); usually lower and central stripe uniting near the caudal base, spot on caudal base often somewhat disconnected from stripe; caudal fin with or without semicircular bars; total length up to 8.2 cm...- **19**

17b Dwarf species (total length up to some 7 cm, including a 3 cm long caudal fin!) with dusky (highly) pointed unpaired fins; reddish brown or covered by strong iridescence (especially in males); central stripe with a dark lateral blotch (immediately behind the pectoral fins); Kalimantan Barat: Kapuas River basin
Betta dimidiata ROBERTS, 1989

17c Caudal fin (at least in fish with branched caudal rays) rhomboid (or at least pointed); branching of caudal rays starts with some 4 cm total length; some fish with central and lower stripes uniting well in advance of caudal base; most males with dark, semicircular markings in the caudal fin: Fig. 2i; total length up to some 14 cm; Borneo, Pulau Natuna Besar ...- **18 (akarensis - species group)**

18a Southwestern Sabah
Betta (akarensis) chini NG, 1993

18b Northeastern Sarawak
Betta (akarensis) akarensis REGAN, 1910

18c Brunei, Sarawak; total length up to some 14 cm
Betta (akarensis) climacura VIERKE, 1984

18d Kalimantan Barat, K. Tengah
Betta (akarensis) sp. D

18e Kalimantan Timur
Betta (akarensis) sp. R

18f Northern Kalimantan Timur, southeastern Sabah: near Tawau
Betta (akarensis) balunga HERRE, 1940

19a Central stripe often with even darker (and slightly broadened) area immediately behind the pectoral fin base; light interspace between the broad upper and central stripe: thin, about half a scale wide (thus looking like a thin, light stripe on a dusky body); elongate species; total length up to some 5 cm (the caudal fin is usually pointed in adult males); Kalimantan Barat: Kapuas River basin
Betta dimidiata ROBERTS, 1989

19b Light interspace broader, about one scale wide; slender or stout species; total length up to 8.2 cm...- **20**

20a Males with delicate semicircular bars in the caudal fin (females with series of spots instead) as in Fig. 8 (but caudal fin rounded); in adults, often an uppermost stripe visible, giving a total of four stripes on the body ...- **22 (edithae - species group)**

20b Males with anal and caudal fins with broad, blue or dark margin, especially in males: Fig. 5; three stripes...- **21 (picta - species group)**

21a Southeastern Thailand, southern Cambodia, southern Viet Nam; iridescence not clearly confined to fin margins of males: especially covering the caudal fin almost completely
Betta (picta) prima KOTTELAT, 1994

21b Malay Peninsula, southern Thailand; colour pattern resembling Betta taeniata in males (females with little iridescence); total length up to 6 cm
Betta (picta) simplex KOTTELAT, 1994

21c Borneo: Sarawak; no colour differences between males and females; fin margins and gill covers iridescent in light blue; large species: total length up to some 8 cm
Betta (picta) taeniata REGAN, 1910

© Verlag A.C.S. GmbH

21d Java, Sumatra, (Malay Peninsula ?); males only have broadly bordered fins and gill covers in darker iridescent blue; total length up to some 6 cm
Betta (picta) picta (VALENCIENNES, in CUVIER & VALENCIENNES, 1846)

22a Gill membrane and posterior part of gill cover somewhat transparent; in holding males, brood is visible through the throat; total length up to some 5 cm; Sumatra: Jambi
Betta (edithae) sp. "Jambi (Sumatra: Hari)"

22b Branchiogestial membrane and gill cover translucent or opaque; total length up to 8.2 cm; Borneo: Kalimantan Timur, K. Selatan, K. Tengah, K. Barat, Sumatra: Way Kambas, Malay Peninsula (?)
Betta (edithae) edithae VIERKE, 1984 s.l.

23a Caudal fin much longer than head length: domestic stock of :
Betta (splendens) splendens REGAN, 1910
Betta (splendens) imbellis LADIGES, 1975

23b Caudal fin less than twice of head length...- **24**

24a Smaller species: total length up to 7 cm; caudal fin rounded: Fig. 2a-b (only the foerschi species group from Borneo sometimes with one elongated ray forming a single extension which stands out sharply from the margin)...- **26**

24b Large species: total length up to 11 cm; in adults and subadults, caudal fin somewhat rhomboid with a few long, filamentous central rays: Fig. 13; Malay Peninsula, Sumatra, Banka...- **25 (bellica - species group)**

Fig. 13

25a Malay Peninsula, northeastern Sumatra; in adults: head slightly convex above the eye and pelvic fin not reaching middle of anal fin; total length up to 11 cm
Betta (bellica) bellica SAUVAGE, 1884

25b Central eastern Sumatra, Banka (?); in adults: head somewhat concave above the eye (resulting in a hump at the nape) and pelvic fin reaching middle of anal fin; total length over 10 cm
Betta (bellica) simorum TAN & TAN, 1996

26a Head with a triangular dark mark below eye: Fig. 14; live colouration unknown; lowlands of northwestern Sumatra (not Lake Toba!); total length up to 5 cm
Betta (splendens) rubra PERUGIA, 1893

Fig. 14

26b Head without triangular mark, below the eye only the unmodified lower stripe (comparable to Fig. 5)...- **27**

27a Gill (branchiostegal) membranes only slightly presented during display (throat pushed down only; if gill covers are spread, membranes not especially exposed); spread dorsal fin with nearly parallel rays, not reaching backwards to caudal fin base if spread; dorsal fin with thin iridescent white margin; body elongate; unpaired fins iridescent blue/green (rays and membranes rarely contrasting throughout their length)...- **29**

27b Males spreading their gill covers and membranes extending beyond them during displays (often including face-to-face threats); if spread out, dorsal fin fan shaped (and reaching backwards to the caudal base); all unpaired fins without a thin iridescent margin; body often not elongate but rather stout; red or brown coloured fin rays usually contrasting with the iridescent membranes between them, especially in caudal and anal fin of males....- **28 [splendens - species group]**

28a Lowlands of northwestern Sumatra; head with a triangular dark mark below eye: Fig. 14; live colouration unknown; total length up to 5 cm.
Betta (splendens) rubra PERUGIA, 1893

28b Northeastern Sumatra, western Borneo?, Malay Peninsula; gill cover of males usually with iridescent scales; total length up to some 5 cm.
Betta (splendens) imbellis LADIGES, 1975

28c Northern Malay Peninsula, central (and eastern?) Thailand [escaped or released domestic stocks throughout Southeast Asia]; gill cover of males usually with reddish bar(s); total length up to some 6 cm.
Betta (splendens) splendens REGAN, 1910

28d Northern to eastern Thailand, Laos, Cambodia (middle & lower Mekong River basin); gill cover of males with iridescent scales; total length up to some 7 cm.
Betta (splendens) smaragdina LADIGES, 1972

28e Lower Mekong River basin (southern Viet Nam); gill cover of males usually with reddish bar(s); total length over 5 cm.
Betta (splendens) cf. splendens

29a Body and unpaired fins of males deep red (body sometimes with stripes); if present, iridescent scales often restricted to a more or less promi-

nent lateral blotch; head small; gill covers sometimes with two reddish (rarely yellow) bars (often quite indistinct); Malay Peninsula, Sumatra, Sarawak, Kalimantan Barat, Kalimantan Tengah
...- **32 [coccina - species group (partially)]**

29b Body and fins quite uniformly dark (sometimes with a faint iridescent blue tinge) but sometimes red colours present in fins (especially in pelvic fin); head small; gill covers never with two distinct bars; southern Malay Peninsula, Pulau Bintan...- **31 [Betta (coccina) persephone s.l.]**

29c Body and fins quite uniformly dark (sometimes with strong blue-green iridescence); head larger, especially in males; gill covers usually with two prominent reddish-yellow bars; Borneo: Kalimantan Barat and K. Tengah; total length up to some 7 cm...- **30 [foerschi - species group]**

30a Kalimantan Tengah: Kahajan River and Sampit River basins.
Betta (foerschi) foerschi VIERKE, 1979

30b Kalimantan Tengah, Kalimantan Barat: Jelai (-Bila) River basin.
Betta (foerschi) strohi SCHALLER & KOTTELAT, 1989

30c Kalimantan Barat: Kapuas River basin and coastal drainages.
Betta (foerschi) cf. strohi

31a Pulau Bintan; slightly more elongate ; total length over 4 cm.
Betta (coccina) miniopinna TAN & TAN, 1994

31b Southwestern Malay Peninsula; slightly less elongate ; total length up to 4.5 cm.
Betta (coccina) persephone SCHALLER, 1986

32a Filamentous pelvic ray bright white (sometimes with a light blue tinge), its base with the same red as the other fin rays or even in lighter red; lateral blotch present or not....- **34**

32b Filamentous ray of pelvic fin with black background colour but sometimes partly covered by greenish iridescence, base of filamentous ray dark red or black; males usually with bright blue/green lateral blotch; eastern Sumatra, western Malay Peninsula....- **33 [Betta (coccina) coccina s.l.]**

33a Malay Peninsula: Selangor; iridescence on body often not restricted to lateral blotch; blotch sometimes present in females too; adult males with longer fins; second longest ray of the pelvic fin nearly extending to the tip of the filamentous ray; total length over 5 cm.
Betta (coccina) livida NG & KOTTELAT, 1992

33b Malay Peninsula (Johore) [this could be a distinct taxon] and eastern Sumatra; lateral blotch well defined, hardly any iridescence on adjacent scales; females never with lateral blotch; second longest pelvic ray distinctly shorter than filamentous ray: Fig. 2a; total length up to 5.6 cm.
Betta (coccina) coccina VIERKE, 1979

34a Usually with lateral spot (even displayed by females) and without iridescent spots in the median fins; northwestern Borneo: Sarawak; total length up to 3.8 cm.
Betta (coccina) brownorum WITTE & SCHMIDT, 1992

34b Usually without lateral spot; if a spot is discernible, then fins with further iridescent spots....- **35**

35a Without iridescent bluegreen spots on basal parts of the unpaired fins; southwestern Borneo: Kalimantan Barat; total length up to 6 cm.
Betta (coccina) rutilans WITTE & KOTTELAT, in KOTTELAT, 1991

35b With blue-green iridescent spots on basal parts of the unpaired fins; total length up to 6 cm....- **36**

36a Eastern Malay Peninsula: Pahang; striped colour pattern during display; iridescence on body not present or faint; total length up to 6 cm.
Betta (coccina) tussyae SCHALLER, 1985

36b Banka; uniform red background colour with some blue-green iridescence during display; total length up to 6 cm.
Betta (coccina) burdigala KOTTELAT & NG, 1994

36c Kalimantan Tengah; uniform red background colour with strong blue-green iridescence during display; total length up to 6 cm.
Betta (coccina) sp. Pankalanbun

Abbildungen/figures 1-14 nach/after:
Witte, K.-E. & J. Schmidt (1992): Betta brownorum, a new species of anabantoids (Teleostei: Belontiidae) from northwestern Borneo, with a key to the genus. Ichthyol. Explor. Freshwaters, Vol. 2, No.4, pp. 305-330.
Mit freundl. Genehmigung/with kind permission des Verlags Dr. Friedrich Pfeil, München.

Kai-Erik Witte sagt zum Abgleich von Schlüssel und Buch:

- **Betta (waseri) hipposideros** fehlt im Buch, ist wohl X16245
- **X14005, X14036, X14037** : stimmen mit B. (akarensis) climacura überein, während noch keine Exemplare aus dem Akarfluß zu uns gelangt sind; Akar Mouthbrooder, KEW 426 ist *B. climacura "Kampong Gua Skuat"* & KEW 509 *B. climacura "2km N vom Sg. Rava"*, beide aus Zentral-Sarawak (Matang ist in S-Sarawak).
- **X14255** *B. balunga* nur aus E-Sabah (terra typica: Sg. Balung = Balung Mouthbrooder) und N-Kalimantan Timur
- **X14615** W ist wahrscheinlich *B. (coccina)* sp. Pankalanbun
- **X15005** VIERKE´s Bild zeigt nicht B. (coccina) coccina (*B. (coccina) brownorum*?)
- Als **B. fusca** werden derzeit vielfach Arten aus der *schalleri -* Gruppe bezeichnet, während früher *B. (pugnax)* sp. G von Sumatra so genannt wurde - beides ist eher unwahrscheinlich, aber derzeit nicht auszuschließen
- **X15555, X15556, X15557** entsprechen *B. (schalleri)* sp. E
- **X16245** *B. macrophthalma* kann aufgrund der Wirbel- und Pterygiophorenzahlen nicht zur *waseri*-Gruppe gehören und ist offenbar ein Synonym zu *B. (pugnax) pugnax*
- **X16857** hat nichts mit *B. patoti* zu tun= *B. (unimaculata)* sp. "Pulau Laut" ; die Insel gehört zu Kal. Selatan, der Fisch ohne Bauchflossen ist eine Mutante
- **X17695** Nur die Fotos von LINKE zeigen *B. schalleri* s.str. von Banka
- **X18115** = *B. (akarensis)* sp. D
- **X18128** ist ein *B. (akarensis) climacura* von Matang nahe Kuching, S-Sarawak
- **X14616** W ist ein sicheres M (dann s. für W X14615)
- **X18130** ist identisch mit X16856
- **X18135** = *B. (patoti)* sp. "Sangau"
- **X18136** ist ein weiterer *B. (akarensis) climacura* aus Sarawak

Kai-Erik Witte´s comments on book and key:

- **Betta (waseri) hipposideros** *is missing, probably X16245*
- **X14005, X14036, X14037** : *are identic with B. (akarensis) climacura; no speciemen from Akar River reached us alive until today; Akar Mouthbrooder; KEW 426 is B. (akarensis) climacura "Kampong Gua Skuat" & KEW 509 B. (akarensis) climacura "2km N vom Sg. Rava", both from C-Sarawak (Matang is in S-Sarawak).*
- **X14255** *B. balunga only from E-Sabah (terra typica: Sg. Balung = Balung Mouthbrooder) and N-Kalimantan Timur*
- **X14615** *W is probably B. (coccina) sp. Pankalanbun*
- **X15005** VIERKE´s *picture does not show B. (coccina) coccina; maybe B. (coccina) brownorum (?)*
- **B. fusca** *is a name often used for species of the schalleri - group ; in the past B. (pugnax) sp. G from Sumatra was called B. fusca - both seems to be unlikely, but cannot be decided yet.*
- **X15555, X15556, X15557** *are B. (schalleri) sp. E*
- **X16245** *B. macrophthalma: this species cannot belong to the waseri-group due to vertebral and pterygiophoral counts and seems to be a synonym of B. (pugnax) pugnax*
- **X16857** *is not B. patoti but B. (unimaculata) sp. "Pulau Laut" ; the island belongs to Kal. Selatan, the fish without ventral fins is a mutant*
- **X17695** *only the pictures of LINKE shows B. schalleri s.str. from Banka*
- **X18115** = *B. (akarensis) sp. D*
- **X18128** *is B. (akarensis) climacura from Matang near Kuching, S-Sarawak*
- **X14616** *W is a M (see for W X14615)*
- **X18130** *is identic with X16856*
- **X18135** = *B. (patoti) sp. "Sangau"*
- **X18136** *is one more B. (akarensis) climacura from Sarawak*

Die Vielfalt der Formen und Farben bei Kampffischen der Art *Betta splendens* erscheint unüberschaubar. Dennoch lassen sich bestimmte Standards in Farbe und Beflossung unterscheiden. Wir haben für den Fall, daß diese Fische sortiert angeboten werden, Code-Nummern entwickelt, die wir Ihnen hier vorstellen.

The varieties of forms and colours in the species of the Fighters (Betta splendens) are literally countless. Still, certain standards can be set up in terms of colouration and shape of the fins. In case the fish are offered sorted, we can help you to identify them with the code-number-system introduced here.

Rundschwanz / Roundtail

- black: X18495
- blue: X18475
- green/turquise: X18485
- multicoloured: X18480
- red: X18490
- white: X18500

Stutzschwanz / Cuttail

- black: X18360
- blue: X18340
- green/turquise: X18350
- multicoloured: X18345
- red: X18355
- white: X18365

Schleierschwanz / Fantail

- black: X18525
- blue: X18505
- green/turquise: X18515
- multicoloured: X18510
- red: X18520
- white: X18530

Kammschwanz / Combtail

- black: X18390
- blue: X18370
- green/turquise: X18380
- multicoloured: X18375
- red: X18385
- white: X18395

Lanzenschwanz / Lancettail

- black: X18455
- blue: X18435
- green/turquise: X18445
- multicoloured: X18440
- red: X18450
- white: X18460

Doppelschwanz / Doubletail

- black: X18330
- blue: X18310
- green/turquise: X18320
- multicoloured: X18315
- red: X18325
- white: X18335

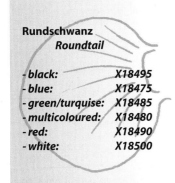

Hintergrundzeichnungen nach VIERKE, 19
Backgrounddrawings after VIERKE, 1978, ch

© **Verlag A.C.S. GmbH**

X05555-4 Anabas oligolepis BLEEKER, 1855
High bodied Climbing Perch   ADULT
South of Asia: India and BanglaDesh, W, 15 - 20 cm
Photo: Horst Linke

X05705-3 Anabas testudineus testudineus (BLOCH, 1795)
Climbing Perch   JUVENIL
Tropical Asia, W, 12-20 cm
Photo: F.Teigler/ Archiv ACS

X05705-4 Anabas testudineus testudineus (BLOCH, 1795)
Climbing Perch   ADULT
Tropical Asia, W, 12 - 20 cm
Photo: Horst Linke

X05715-4 Anabas testudineus "AYER HITAM"
Climbing Perch   Land-walking   ADULT
Malaysia, W, 12 - 20 cm
Photo: J. Vierke

X05746-4 Anabas testudineus "PADANG"
Climbing Perch   Portrait   ADULT
E-Sumatra, W, 12 - 20 cm
Photo: F. Schäfer

X13005-4 Belontia hasselti (CUVIER, 1831)
Java Combtail   MALE   ADULT
Sumatra , Borneo, Malaysia, W, 15 - 20 cm
Photo: U. Werner

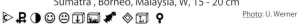

X13005-4 Belontia hasselti (CUVIER, 1831)
Java Combtail   FEMALE   ADULT
Sumatra , Borneo, Malaysia, W, 15 - 20 cm
Photo: U. Werner

X13005-4 Belontia hasselti (CUVIER, 1831)
Java Combtail   MALE   ADULT
Sumatra, Borneo, Malaysia, W, 15 - 20 cm
Photo: U. Werner

X13105-5 Belontia signata signata (GÜNTHER, 1861)
Combtail MALE ADULT
Sri Lanka, W, 15 cm
Photo: G. Kopic

X13105-4 Belontia signata signata (GÜNTHER, 1861)
Combtail FEMALE ADULT
Sri Lanka, W, 15 cm
Photo: ACS Migge/Reinhard

X13115-3 Belontia signata jonklaasi
Pectoral Spot Combtail MALE JUVENIL
Sri Lanka, W, 15 cm
Photo: F. Teigler/ Archiv ACS

X13115-3 Belontia signata jonklaasi
Pectoral Spot Combtail FEMALE JUVENIL
Sri Lanka, W, 15 cm
Photo: F. Teigler/ Archiv ACS

X13115-4 Belontia signata jonklaasi
Pectoral Spot Combtail MALE ADULT
Sri Lanka, W, 15 cm
Photo: ACS/ Migge/Reinhard

X13115-4 Belontia signata jonklaasi
Pectoral Spot Combtail FEMALE ADULT
Sri Lanka, W, 15 cm
Photo: ACS/ Migge/Reinhard

X13125-4 Belontia signata "KOTTAWA FOREST"
Combtail MALE ADULT
Sri Lanka: Kottawa Forest, W, 15 cm
Photo: H.-J. Günther

X13125-4 Belontia signata "KOTTAWA FOREST"
Combtail FEMALE ADULT
Sri Lanka: Kottawa Forest, W, 15 cm
Photo: H.-J. Günther

© Verlag A.C.S. GmbH

X14005-4 Betta akarensis REGAN, 1910
  Akara Mouthbrooder   MALE   ADULT
  Borneo: NE-Sarawak (this form: 426 Matang), W, 12 cm
▷ ⫫P ◑ ☺ ☹ ⎗ 🖼 🐟 ◈ ⎗ ♂
Photo: J. Schmidt

X14005-4 Betta akarensis REGAN, 1910
  Akara Mouthbrooder   FEMALE   ADULT
  Borneo: NE-Sarawak (this form: 426 Matang), W, 12 cm
▷ ⫫P ◑ ☺ ☹ ⎗ 🖼 🐟 ◈ ⎗ ♀
Photo: J. Schmidt

X14036-4 Betta akarensis REGAN, 1910
  Akara Mouthbrooder Var.I   JUVENIL
  Borneo: NE-Sarawak (this form: 426 Matang), W, 12 cm
▷ ⫫P ◑ ☺ ☹ ⎗ 🖼 🐟 ◈ ⎗
Photo: J. Schmidt

X14036-4 Betta akarensis REGAN, 1910
  Akara Mouthbrooder Var.I   MALE   ADULT
  Borneo: NE-Sarawak (this form: 509 Matang), W, 12 cm
▷ ⫫P ◑ ☺ ☹ ⎗ 🖼 🐟 ◈ ⎗ ♂
Photo: J. Schmidt

X14037-4 Betta akarensis REGAN, 1910
  Akara Mouthbrooder Var.II   FEMALE   ADULT
  Borneo: Brunei, Peat Swamps, W, 12 cm
▷ ⫫P ◑ ☺ ☹ ⎗ 🖼 🐟 ◈ ⎗ ♀
Photo: P. K. L. Ng

X14105-4 Betta albimarginata KOTTELAT & NG, 1994
  Whiteseam Fighter   MALE   ADULT
  Borneo: N-Kalimantan Timur: Sebuku-River, W, 5 cm
▷ ⫫P ● ☺ ☹ ⎗ 🖼 ⚠ Ⓢ ♂
Photo: P. K. L. Ng

X14105-4 Betta albimarginata KOTTELAT & NG, 1994
  Whiteseam Fighter   MALE   ADULT
  Borneo: N-Kalimantan Timur: Sebuku-River, W, 5 cm
▷ ⫫P ● ☺ ☹ ⎗ 🖼 ⚠ Ⓢ ♂
Photo: M. Kottelat

X14105-4 Betta albimarginata KOTTELAT & NG, 1994
  Whiteseam Fighter   PORTRAIT   a mouthbrooder ???
  Borneo: N-Kalimantan Timur: Sebuku-River, W, 5 cm
▷ ⫫P ● ☺ ☹ ⎗ 🖼 ⚠ Ⓢ ♂
Photo:P. K. L. Ng

X14175-3 Betta anabatoides BLEEKER, 1851
Large Unspotted Mouthbrooder SUBADULT
Borneo: Kalimantan-Tengah, Kubu, W, 13 cm
Photo: G. Kopic

X14185-4 Betta cf. anabatoides (see also page 38)
Large Unspotted Mouthbrooder FEMALE ADULT
Borneo: Kalimantan-Tengah, W, 13 cm
Photo: H. Linke

X14255-4 Betta balunga HERRE, 1940
Balunga Mouthbrooder MALE ADULT
Borneo: Kalimantan (this fish from terra typica), W, 14 cm
Photo: J. Schmidt

X14255-4 Betta balunga HERRE, 1940
Balunga Mouthbrooder MALE ADULT
Borneo: Kalimantan barat, W, 14 cm
Photo: P. K. L. Ng

X14255-4 Betta balunga HERRE, 1940
Balunga Mouthbrooder FEMALE ADULT
Borneo: Kalimantan barat, W, 14 cm
Photo: H. Linke

X14325-4 Betta bellica SAUVAGE, 1884
Slender Betta MALE ADULT
Malaysia, NE-Sumatra, W, 11 cm
Photo: H. Linke

X14325-4 Betta bellica SAUVAGE, 1884
Slender Betta FEMALE ADULT
Malaysia, NE-Sumatra, W, 11 cm
Photo: H. Linke

X14336-3 Betta cf. bellica
Slender Betta SUBADULT
Malaysia, W, 11 cm
Photo: J. Schmidt

© Verlag A.C.S. GmbH

X14337-4 Betta bellica "MUAR"
Slender Betta   MALE   ADULT
Malaysia, W, 11 cm
▷ ⵏP ◑ ☺ ☺ 🔄 🖼 🐛 ◈ 🔳 ♂   Photo: J. Schmidt

X14337-4 Betta bellica "MUAR"
Slender Betta   FEMALE   ADULT
Malaysia, W, 11 cm
▷ ⵏP ◑ ☺ ☺ 🔄 🖼 🐛 ◈ 🔳 ♀   Photo: J. Schmidt

X14325-3 Betta bellica SAUVAGE, 1884
Slender Betta   SUBADULT
Malaysia: Pontian, W, 11 cm
▷ ⵏP ◑ ☺ ☺ 🔄 🖼 🐛 ◈ 🔳   Photo: P. K. L. Ng

X14505-4 Betta brownorum WITTE & SCHMIDT, 1992
Browns Red Dwarf Fighter   MALE   ADULT
Borneo: Sarawak , W, 4 cm
▷ ⵏP ◑ ☺ ☺ 🔄 🖼 🐛 ⚠ 🆂 ♂   Photo: P. K. L. Ng

X14505-4 Betta brownorum WITTE & SCHMIDT, 1992
Browns Red Dwarf Fighter   MALE   ADULT
Borneo: Sarawak (this fish from terra typica), W, 4 cm
▷ ⵏP ◑ ☺ ☺ 🔄 🖼 🐛 ⚠ 🆂 ♂   Photo: J. Schmidt

X14505-4 Betta brownorum WITTE & SCHMIDT, 1992
Browns Red Dwarf Fighter   FEMALE   ADULT
Borneo: Sarawak (this fish from terra typica), W, 4 cm
▷ ⵏP ◑ ☺ ☺ 🔄 🖼 🐛 ⚠ 🆂 ♀   Photo: J. Schmidt

X14516-4 Betta brownorum "MATANG"
Browns Red Dwarf Fighter   MALE   ADULT
Borneo: Sarawak , W, 4 cm
▷ ⵏP ◑ ☺ ☺ 🔄 🖼 🐛 ⚠ 🆂 ♂   Photo: J. Schmidt

X14516-4 Betta brownorum "MATANG"
Browns Red Dwarf Fighter   FEMALE   ADULT
Borneo: Sarawak , W, 4 cm
▷ ⵏP ◑ ☺ ☺ 🔄 🖼 🐛 ⚠ 🆂 ♀   Photo: J. Schmidt

X14615-4 Betta burdigala KOTTELAT & NG, 1994
Red brown Dwarf Fighter   MALE   ADULT
Indonesia: Banka, W, 6 cm

▷ ℙ ◑ ☺ ☹ ⬇ 🖼 🦐 ⚠ Ⓢ ♂   Photo: H. Linke

X14615-4 Betta burdigala KOTTELAT & NG, 1994
Red brown Dwarf Fighter   FEMALE   ADULT
Indonesia: Banka, W, 6 cm

▷ ℙ ◑ ☺ ☹ ⬇ 🖼 🦐 ⚠ Ⓢ ♀   Photo: G. Kopic

X14615-4 Betta burdigala KOTTELAT & NG, 1994
Red brown Dwarf Fighter   MALE   ADULT
Indonesia: Banka, W, 6 cm

▷ ℙ ◑ ☺ ☹ ⬇ 🖼 ⚠ Ⓢ ♂   Photo: P. K. L. Ng

X14655   Betta channoides KOTTELAT & NG, 1994 (preserved specimen)
Snakehead fighter   living unknown
Borneo: Central Kalimantan Timur, W, 5 cm (?)

Photo: M. Kottelat

X14715-4 Betta chini NG, 1993
Chini Mouthbrooder   MALE   ADULT
Borneo: NW-Sabah: Beaufort, W, 14 cm

▷ ℙ ◐ ☺ ☹ ⬇ 🖼 🐟 ◈ ⊡ ♂   Photo: P. K. L. Ng

X14715-4 Betta chini NG, 1993
Chini Mouthbrooder   FEMALE   ADULT
Borneo: NW-Sabah, W, 14 cm

▷ ℙ ◐ ☺ ☹ ⬇ 🖼 🐟 ◈ ⊡ ♀   Photo: H. Linke

X14815-3 Betta chloropharynx KOTTELAT & NG, 1994
Greenthroat Mouthbrooder   MALE   ADULT
Indonesia: Banka, W, 14 cm

▷ ℙ ◐ ☺ ☹ ⬇ 🖼 🐟 ◈ ⊡ ♂   Photo: P. K. L. Ng

X14815-4 Betta chloropharynx KOTTELAT & NG, 1994
Greenthroat Mouthbrooder   MALE   ADULT
Indonesia: Banka, W, 14 cm

▷ ℙ ◐ ☺ ☹ ⬇ 🖼 🐟 ◈ ⊡ ♂   Photo: H. Linke

X14915-5 Betta climacura VIERKE, 1984
Ladder Mouthbrooder MALE ADULT
Borneo: Brunei, Sarawak, W, 14 cm
▷ ⑫ ◑ ☺ ☹ ⏏ 🖼 🐟 ◈ ⊡ ♂   Photo: J. Vierke

X14915-4 Betta climacura VIERKE, 1984
Ladder Mouthbrooder PAIR ADULT
Borneo: Brunei, Sarawak, W, 14 cm
▷ ⑫ ◑ ☺ ☹ ⏏ 🖼 🐟 ◈ ⊡ ♂ ♀   Photo: J. Vierke

X15005-4 Betta coccina VIERKE, 1979
Vine red Fighter MALE ADULT
Sumatra: Jambi, W, 5,5 cm
▷ ⑫ ◐ ☺ ☹ ⊡ 🖼 🦎 ⚠ ⑤ ♂   Photo: H. Linke

X15005-4 Betta coccina VIERKE, 1979
Vine red Fighter PAIR ADULT
Sumatra: Jambi, W, 5,5 cm
▷ ⑫ ◐ ☺ ☹ ⊡ 🖼 🦎 ⚠ ⑤ ♂ ♀   Photo: J. Vierke

X15015-4 Betta coccina "MUAR"
Vine red Fighter MALE ADULT
Malaysia: Johore, W, 5,5 cm
▷ ⑫ ◐ ☺ ☹ ⊡ 🖼 🦎 ⚠ ⑤ ♂   Photo: J. Schmidt

X15015-4 Betta coccina "MUAR"
Vine red Fighter FEMALE ADULT
Malaysia: Johore, W, 5,5 cm
▷ ⑫ ◐ ☺ ☹ ⊡ 🖼 🦎 ⚠ ⑤ ♀   Photo: J. Schmidt

X15006-4 Betta cf. coccina "LANCET-FIN"
Vine red Fighter MALE ADULT
Indonesia: commercial import, W, 6 cm
▷ ⑫ ◐ ☺ ☹ ⊡ 🖼 🦎 ⚠ ⑤ ♂   Photo: F. Teigler/ Archiv ACS

X15006-4 Betta cf. coccina"LANCET-FIN"
Vine red Fighter FEMALE ADULT
Indonesia: commercial import, W, 6 cm
▷ ⑫ ◐ ☺ ☹ ⊡ 🖼 🦎 ⚠ ⑤ ♀   Photo: F. Teigler/ Archiv ACS

X18510-5 Betta splendens "FANTAIL MULTICOLOUR"   MALE

Photo: L. Seegers

© Verlag A.C.S. GmbH

X17915-5 Betta smaragdina   MALE

Photo: L. Seegers

X15125-4 Betta dimidiata ROBERTS, 1989
Dwarf Mouthbrooder MALE ADULT
Borneo: Kalimantan barat, W, 7 cm

▷ ⅍ ◐ ☺ ☺ ⊞ ▦ ➤ ⚠ ⑤ ♂
Photo: H. Linke

X15125-4 Betta dimidiata ROBERTS, 1989
Dwarf Mouthbrooder FEMALE ADULT
Borneo: Kalimantan barat, W, 7 cm

▷ ⅍ ◐ ☺ ☺ ⊞ ▦ ➤ ⚠ ⑤ ♀
Photo: G. Kopic

X15135-4 Betta dimidiata "KAPUAS"
Dwarf Mouthbrooder MALE ADULT
Borneo: Kalimantan barat, W, 7 cm

▷ ⅍ ◐ ☺ ☺ ⊞ ▦ ➤ ⚠ ⑤ ♂
Photo: P. K. L. Ng

X15245-4 Betta edithae VIERKE, 1984
Ediths Mouthbrooder MALE ADULT
Borneo, Sumatra, Malaysia, W, 8,5 cm

▷ ⅍ ◑ ☺ ☺ ⊞ ▦ ➤ ◈ ▦ ♂
Photo: H.-G. Evers

X15245-4 Betta edithae VIERKE, 1984
Ediths Mouthbrooder FEMALE ADULT
Borneo, Sumatra, Malaysia, W, 8,5 cm

▷ ⅍ ◑ ☺ ☺ ⊞ ▦ ➤ ◈ ▦ ♀
Photo: H.-G. Evers

X15265-4 Betta edithae "BANGKA"
Ediths Mouthbrooder MALE ADULT
Indonesia: Bangka, W, 8,5 cm

▷ ⅍ ◑ ☺ ☺ ⊞ ▦ ➤ ◈ ▦ ♂
Photo: H. Linke

X15266-4 Betta edithae "LIANG ANGANG"
Ediths Mouthbrooder MALE ADULT
Borneo, W, 8,5 cm

▷ ⅍ ◑ ☺ ☺ ⊞ ▦ ➤ ◈ ▦ ♂
Photo: J. Schmidt

X15355-4 Betta enisae KOTTELAT, 1995 (see also page 40)
Blue band Mouthbrooder MALE ADULT
Borneo: Kalimantan barat, W, 8 cm

▷ ⅍ ◐ ☺ ☺ ⊞ ▦ ➤ ◈ ▦ ♂
Photo: J. Schmidt

© **Verlag A.C.S. GmbH**

X15355-4 Betta enisae KOTTELAT, 1995 (see also page 40)
Blue band Mouthbrooder   MALE   ADULT
Borneo: Kapuas, W, 8 cm

▷ ⫟P ● ☺ ☻ ⎗ ⊠ ➤ ◈ ⎕ ♂   Photo: P. K. L. Ng

X15405-4 Betta foerschi VIERKE, 1979
Foerschs Mouthbrooder   MALE   ADULT
Borneo: Kalimantan tengah, W, 7 cm

▷ ⫟P ● ☺ ☻ ⎗ ⊠ ➤ ⚠ ⎕ ♂   Photo: H. Linke

X15405-4 Betta foerschi VIERKE, 1979
Foerschs Mouthbrooder   FEMALE   ADULT
Borneo: Kalimantan tengah, W, 7 cm

▷ ⫟P ● ☺ ☻ ⎗ ⊠ ➤ ⚠ ⎕ ♀   Photo: G. Kopic

X15555-4 Betta fusca REGAN, 1910
Brown Mouthbrooder   MALE   ADULT
Indonesia: Sumatra, W, 12 cm

▷ ⫟P ◑ ☺ ☻ ⎗ ⊠ ➤ ◈ ⎕ ♂   Photo: H. Linke

X15556-4 Betta fusca "SUMATRA"
Brown Mouthbrooder   MALE   ADULT
Indonesia: Sumatra, W, 12 cm

▷ ⫟P ◑ ☺ ☻ ⎗ ⊠ ➤ ◈ ⎕ ♂   Photo: J. Schmidt

X15556-4 Betta fusca "SUMATRA"
Brown Mouthbrooder   FEMALE   ADULT
Indonesia: Sumatra, W, 12 cm

▷ ⫟P ◑ ☺ ☻ ⎗ ⊠ ➤ ◈ ⎕ ♀   Photo: J. Schmidt

X15557-4 Betta fusca "SUNGAI STUNGANG" (= B. schalleri?)
Brown Mouthbrooder   MALE   ADULT
Indonesia: Borneo, W, 12 cm

▷ ⫟P ◑ ☺ ☻ ⎗ ⊠ ➤ ◈ ⎕ ♂   Photo: J. Schmidt

X15557-4 Betta fusca "SUNGAI STUNGANG" (= B. schalleri?)
Brown Mouthbrooder   FEMALE   ADULT
Indonesia: Borneo, W, 12 cm

▷ ⫟P ◑ ☺ ☻ ⎗ ⊠ ➤ ◈ ⎕ ♀   Photo: J. Schmidt

X15875-4 Betta imbellis LADIGES, 1975
Crescent Betta MALE ADULT
Malaysia, NE-Sumatra, W-Borneo (?), W, 5 cm
Photo: ACS Migge/Reinhard

X15875-4 Betta imbellis LADIGES, 1975
Crescent Betta FEMALE ADULT
Malaysia, NE-Sumatra, W-Borneo (?), W, 5 cm
Photo: ACS Migge/Reinhard

X15875-4 Betta imbellis LADIGES, 1975 Breeding colour
Crescent Betta MALE ADULT
Malaysia, NE-Sumatra, W-Borneo (?), W, 5 cm
Photo: G. Kopic

X15876-5 Betta imbellis "FANTAIL"
Crescent Betta MALE ADULT
Breeding-Form, B, 6 cm
Photo: J. Schmidt

X15886-4 Betta imbellis "KO SAMUI" endangered variety!
Crescent Betta MALE ADULT
Thailand: Ko Samui island, W, 5 cm
Photo: J. Schmidt

X15886-4 Betta imbellis "KO SAMUI" endangered variety!
Crescent Betta FEMALE ADULT
Thailand: Ko Samui island, W, 5 cm
Photo: J. Schmidt

X15896-4 Betta imbellis "PENANG"
Crescent Betta MALE ADULT
Malaysia: Penang island, W, 5 cm
Photo: J. Schmidt

X15896-4 Betta imbellis "PENANG"
Crescent Betta FEMALE ADULT
Malaysia: Penang island, W, 5 cm
Photo: J. Schmidt

© Verlag A.C.S. GmbH

Photo: F. Schäfer

Photo: F. Schäfer

1. Sumatra: Bachlauf mit dichter Uferböschung
   Sumatra: small stream with thicket along its bank

2. Im Dickicht der Sumpfpflanzen (blühend: Eichhornia)
   leben oft kleine Labyrinthfische
   *In the marsh plants (blooming: Eichhornia) often live
   small Labyrinths*

X 17368-5 Betta pugnax "PENANG"   MALE   Malaysia: Penang island

Photo: H. Linke

© **Verlag A.C.S. GmbH**

X16145-3 Betta livida NG & KOTTELAT, 1992
Selangor Red Fighter   SUBADULT
Malaysia: Selangor, W, 5 cm

▷ ⫟P ◐ ☺ ☺ ⊡ 🔊 🦗 ⚠ ⑤   Photo: G. Kopic

X16145-4 Betta livida NG & KOTTELAT, 1992
Selangor Red Fighter   MALE   ADULT
Malaysia: Selangor, W, 5 cm

▷ ⫟P ◐ ☺ ☺ ⊡ 🔊 🦗 ⚠ ⑤ ♂   Photo: P. K. L. Ng

X16245-4 Betta macrophthalma REGAN, 1910
Big Eye Mouthbrooder   MALE   ADULT
Malaysia; W, 14 cm

▷ ⫟P ◑ ☺ ☺ ⊡ 🔊 ➡: ◈ ⊡ ♂   Photo: J. Schmidt

X16245-4 Betta macrophthalma REGAN, 1910
Big Eye Mouthbrooder   FEMALE   ADULT
Malaysia; W, 14 cm

▷ ⫟P ◑ ☺ ☺ ⊡ 🔊 ➡: ◈ ⊡ ♀   Photo: J. Schmidt

X16246-4 Betta macrophthalma REGAN, 1910
Big Eye Mouthbrooder VAR.I   PAIR   ADULT
Malaysia: Pekan Nenas, W, 14 cm

▷ ⫟P ◑ ☺ ☺ ⊡ 🔊 ➡: ◈ ⊡ ♂ ♀   Photo: J. Schmidt

X16246-4 Betta macrophthalma REGAN, 1910
Big Eye Mouthbrooder VAR.I   FEMALE   ADULT
Malaysia: Pekan Nenas, W, 14 cm

▷ ⫟P ◑ ☺ ☺ ⊡ 🔊 ➡: ◈ ⊡ ♀   Photo: J. Schmidt

X16345-4 Betta macrostoma REGAN, 1910
Peacock Mouthbrooder   MALE   ADULT
Borneo: Brunei, W, 14 cm

▷ ⫟P ◑ ☺ ☺ ⊡ 🔊 ➡: ⚠ ⊡ ♂   Photo: D. Bork

X16345-4 Betta macrostoma REGAN, 1910
Peacock Mouthbrooder   FEMALE   ADULT
Borneo: Brunei, W, 14 cm

▷ ⫟P ◑ ☺ ☺ ⊡ 🔊 ➡: ⚠ ⊡ ♀   Photo: D. Bork

X16356-4 Betta macrostoma REGAN, 1910
Peacock Mouthbrooder "RED" MALE ADULT
Borneo: Brunei, W, 14 cm

▷ ⫯P ◑ ☺ ☻ 🎛 🖼 🐛 ⚠ Ⓢ ♂   Photo: J. Schmidt

X16356-4 Betta macrostoma REGAN, 1910
Peacock Mouthbrooder "RED" FEMALE ADULT
Borneo: Brunei, W, 14 cm

▷ ⫯P ◑ ☺ ☻ 🎛 🖼 🐛 ⚠ Ⓢ ♀   Photo: J. Schmidt

X16455-4 Betta miniopinna TAN & TAN, 1994
Small fin Fighter MALE ADULT
Pulau Bintan, W, 4 cm

▷ ⫯P ◑ ☺ ☻ 🎛 🖼 🐛 ⚠ Ⓢ ♂   Photo: P. K. l. Ng

X16455-4 Betta miniopinna TAN & TAN, 1994
Small fin Fighter FEMALE ADULT
Pulau Bintan, W, 4 cm

▷ ⫯P ◑ ☺ ☻ 🎛 🖼 🐛 ⚠ Ⓢ ♀   Photo: H. Linke

X16755-3 Betta ocellata DeBEAUFORT, 1933
Eyespot Mouthbrooder MALE SUBADULT
Tawau, W, 12 cm

▷ ⫯P ◐ ☺ ☻ 🎛 🖼 ➤ ◈ 🕇 ♂   Photo: P. K. L. Ng

X16857-3 Betta cf. patoti
Ventralless Mouthbrooder SUBADULT
Borneo: Kalimantan Timur, W, 12 cm

▷ ⫯P ◐ ☺ ☻ 🎛 🖼 ➤ ◈ 🕇   Photo: J. Schmidt

X16856-4 Betta cf. patoti
Dark Mouthbrooder MALE ADULT
Borneo: Kalimantan Timur, W, 12 cm

▷ ⫯P ◐ ☺ ☻ 🎛 🖼 ➤ ◈ 🕇 ♂   Photo: J. Schmidt

X16975-4 Betta persephone SCHALLER, 1986
Black Small Fighter MALE ADULT
SW-Malaysia, W, 4 cm

▷ ⫯P ◑ ☺ ☻ 🎛 🖼 🐛 ⚠ Ⓢ ♂   Photo: H. Linke

© Verlag A.C.S. GmbH

X16975-4 Betta persephone SCHALLER, 1986
Black Small Fighter   MALE   ADULT
SW-Malaysia (this fish from terra typica), W, 4 cm
▷ ⱿP ◑ ☺ ☺ ⊤ ☷ ✦ ⚠ ⑤ ♂   Photo: J. Schmidt

X16975-4 Betta persephone SCHALLER, 1986
Black Small Fighter   FEMALE   ADULT
SW-Malaysia (this fish from terra typica), W, 4 cm
▷ ⱿP ◑ ☺ ☺ ⊤ ☷ ✦ ⚠ ⑤ ♀   Photo: J. Schmidt

X16976-4 Betta persephone „MUAR"
Black Small Fighter   MALE   ADULT
Malaysia: Muar, W, 4 cm
▷ ⱿP ◑ ☺ ☺ ⊤ ☷ ✦ ⚠ ⑤ ♂   Photo: J. Schmidt

X16976-4 Betta persephone „MUAR"
Black Small Fighter   FEMALE   ADULT
Malaysia: Muar, W, 4 cm
▷ ⱿP ◑ ☺ ☺ ⊤ ☷ ✦ ⚠ ⑤ ♀   Photo: J. Schmidt

X17105-4 Betta picta (CUVIER & VALENCIENNES, 1846)
Javan Mouthbrooder   MALE   ADULT
Java (this form), W, 6 cm
▷ Ɀ ◐ ☺ ☺ ⊤ ☷ ➛ ◈ ⓜ ♂   Photo: L. Seegers

X17105-4 Betta picta (CUVIER & VALENCIENNES, 1846)
Javan Mouthbrooder   FEMALE   ADULT
Java (this form), W, 6 cm
▷ Ɀ ◐ ☺ ☺ ⊤ ☷ ➛ ◈ ⓜ ♀   Photo: L. Seegers

X17115-4 Betta picta (CUVIER & VALENCIENNES, 1846)
Javan Mouthbrooder   MALE   ADULT
Sumatra (this form), W, 6 cm
▷ Ɀ ◐ ☺ ☺ ⊤ ☷ ➛ ◈ ⓜ ♂   Photo: J. Vierke

X17115-4 Betta picta (CUVIER & VALENCIENNES, 1846)
Javan Mouthbrooder   FEMALE   ADULT
Sumatra (this form), W, 6 cm
▷ Ɀ ◐ ☺ ☺ ⊤ ☷ ➛ ◈ ⓜ ♀   Photo: J. Vierke

X18475-4 Betta splendens "NORMALFIN BLUE"   MALE   Breeding Form   Photo: H. Linke

X18490-4 Betta splendens "NORMALFIN RED"   MALE   Breeding Form   Photo: H. Linke

X17106-4 Betta picta "MALAYSIA"
Javan Mouthbrooder   MALE   ADULT
S-Malaysia (this form), W, 6 cm
Photo: J. Schmidt

X17225-4 Betta prima KOTTELAT, 1994
Threelined Mouthbrooder   ADULT
SE-Thailand, S-Cambodia, S-Viet Nam, W, 8,5 cm
Photo: H. Linke

X17335-4 Betta pugnax (CANTOR, 1850)
Bukit Merah Mouthbrooder   MALE   ADULT
Malaysia: Bukit Merah (this Form), W, 12 cm
Photo: H. Linke

X17366-4 Betta pugnax (CANTOR, 1850)
Pinang Mouthbrooder   MALE   ADULT
Malaysia: Pinang (this Form), W, 12 cm
Photo: H. Linke

X17367-4 Betta pugnax (CANTOR, 1850)
Puching Mouthbrooder   PAIR   ADULT
Malaysia: Puching (this Form), W, 12 cm
Photo: H. Linke

X17367-4 Betta pugnax (CANTOR, 1850)
Puching Mouthbrooder   FEMALE   ADULT
Malaysia: Puching (this Form), W, 12 cm
Photo: H. Linke

X17375-4 Betta cf. pugnax "FO2"
Brown Operculum Mouthbrooder   MALE   ADULT
Malaysia, W, 12 cm
Photo: J. Schmidt

X17376-4 Betta cf. pugnax „KOTA TINGGI"
Kota Tinggi Mouthbrooder   FEMALE   ADULT
Kota Tinggi, W, 12 cm
Photo: H. Linke

X17377-4 Betta cf. pugnax "TASIK KENYIR"
Tasik Kenyir Mouthbrooder   MALE   ADULT
Tasik Kenyir, W, 10 cm
▷ ⅃P ◑ ☺ ☺ 🔽🔲 ➡ ◈ 🔟 ♂   Photo: J. Schmidt

X17377-4 Betta cf. pugnax "TASIK KENYIR"
Tasik Kenyir Mouthbrooder   MALE   ADULT
Tasik Kenyir, W, 10 cm
▷ ⅃P ◑ ☺ ☺ 🔽🔲 ➡ ◈ 🔟 ♂   Photo: J. Schmidt

X17325-3 Betta cf. pugnax "BORI PAT"
Bori Pat Mouthbrooder   SUBADULT
Malaysia: Bori Pat, W, 8 cm (?)
▷ ⅃P ◑ ☺ ☺ 🔽🔲 ➡ ◈ 🔟   Photo: E. Schraml

X17365-4 Betta cf. pugnax "MERSING"
Mersing Mouthbrooder   MALE   ADULT
Malaysia: Mersing, W, 12 cm
▷ ⅃P ◑ ☺ ☺ 🔽🔲 ➡ ◈ 🔟 ♂   Photo: J. Schmidt

X17455-4 Betta pulchra TAN & TAN, 1996
Beauty Mouthbrooder   MALE   ADULT
Malaysia: Johore, W, 10 cm
▷ ⅃P ◑ ☺ ☺ 🔽🔲 ➡ ◈ 🔟 ♂   Photo: P. K. L. Ng

X17495 Betta rubra PERUGIA, 1893 (preserved specimen)
Red Sumatran Fighter   living unknown
NW-Sumatra, W, 5 cm
                                Photo: M. Kottelat

X17595-4 Betta rutilans WITTE & KOTTELAT in KOTTELAT, 1991
Redish Dwarf Fighter   MALE   ADULT
Borneo: Kalimantan Barat, W, 6 cm
▷ ⅃P ◐ ☺ ☺ 🔽🔲 🐛 ⚠ 🅂 ♂   Photo: H. Linke

X17595-4 Betta rutilans WITTE & KOTTELAT in KOTTELAT, 1991
Redish Dwarf Fighter   FEMALE   ADULT
Borneo: Kalimantan Barat, W, 6 cm
▷ ⅃P ◐ ☺ ☺ 🔽🔲 🐛 ⚠ 🅂 ♀   Photo: P. K. L. Ng

X17695-3 Betta schalleri KOTTELAT & NG, 1994
Schallers Mouthbrooder   PAIR   SUBADULT
Sumatra, Kalimantan Barat, Sarawak, W, 12 cm

▷ �𝟒P ◑ ☺ ☻ ⊡ 🖼 🐟 ◈ ⊡ ♂ ♀   Photo: F. Teigler/ Archiv ACS

X17695-4 Betta schalleri KOTTELAT & NG, 1994
Schallers Mouthbrooder   MALE   ADULT
Sumatra, Kalimantan Barat, Sarawak, W, 12 cm

▷ ⟊P ◑ ☺ ☻ ⊡ 🖼 🐟 ◈ ⊡ ♂   Photo: H. Linke

X17695-4 Betta schalleri KOTTELAT & NG, 1994
Schallers Mouthbrooder   FEMALE   ADULT
Sumatra, Kalimantan Barat, Sarawak, W, 12 cm

▷ ⟊P ◑ ☺ ☻ ⊡ 🖼 🐟 ◈ ⊡ ♀   Photo: H. Linke

X17755-4 Betta simorum TAN & TAN, 1996
Simor Fighter   MALE   ADULT
Sumatra, Banka (?), W, 12 cm

▷ ⟊P ◑ ☺ ☻ ⊡ 🖼 🦎 ◈ ⊡ ♂   Photo: F. Teigler/ Archiv ACS

X17755-4 Betta simorum TAN & TAN, 1996
Simor Fighter   PAIR   ADULT
Sumatra, Banka (?), W, 12 cm

▷ ⟊P ◑ ☺ ☻ ⊡ 🖼 🦎 ◈ ⊡ ♂ ♀   Photo:F. Teigler/ Archiv ACS

X17795-4 Betta simplex KOTTELAT, 1994
Simple Mouthbrooder   MALE   ADULT
Malaysia, S-Thailand, W, 6 cm

▷ ⟊P ◑ ☺ ☻ ⊡ 🖼 🐟 ◈ ⊡ ♂   Photo: H. Linke

X17915-3 Betta smaragdina LADIGES, 1972
Smaragd Fighter   MALE   SUBADULT
E-Thailand, Laos, Cambodia, W, 7 cm

▷ ⟊B ◑ ☺ ☻ ⊡ 🖼 🦎 ◈ ⊡ ♂   Photo: F. Teigler/ Archiv ACS

X17915-5 Betta smaragdina LADIGES, 1972
Smaragd Fighter   MALE   ADULT
E-Thailand, Laos, Cambodia, W, 7 cm

▷ ⟊B ◑ ☺ ☻ ⊡ 🖼 🦎 ◈ ⊡ ♂   Photo: G. Kopic

X17916-4 Betta smaragdina "NONG KHAI"
Smaragd Fighter   FEMALE   ADULT
NE-Thailand, W, 7 cm

▷ ♫ ◗ ☺ ☺ ⊡ 🖼 🐛 ◈ ⊞ ♂
Photo: J. Schmidt

X17916-4 Betta smaragdina "NONG KHAI"
Smaragd Fighter   FEMALE   ADULT
NE-Thailand, W, 7 cm

▷ ♫ ◗ ☺ ☺ ⊡ 🖼 🐛 ◈ ⊞ ♀
Photo: J. Schmidt

X18106-4 Betta sp. aff. splendens "AGUTAGA"
Agutaga-Fighter   MALE   ADULT
Agutaga, W, 6 cm

▷ ♫ ◗ ☺ ☺ ⊡ 🖼 🐛 ◈ ⊞ ♂
Photo: H. Linke

X14185-4 Betta sp. aff. anabatoides (see also page 20)
Large Mouthbrooder   MALE   ADULT
Borneo: Sungai Penjuh, Anjungan, W, 12 cm

▷ ▯P ◗ ☺ ☺ ⊡ 🖼 🐟 ◈ ⊞ ♂
Photo: H. Linke

X14185-4 Betta sp. aff. anabatoides (see also page 20)
Large Mouthbrooder   FEMALE   ADULT
Borneo: Sungai Penjuh, Anjungan, W, 12 cm

▷ ▯P ◗ ☺ ☺ ⊡ 🖼 🐟 ◈ ⊞ ♀
Photo: H. Linke

X15275-4 Betta sp. aff. edithae
New Ediths Mouthbrooder   MALE   ADULT
Sakkamara, W, 8 cm

▷ ▯P ◗ ☺ ☺ ⊡ 🖼 🐟 ◈ ⊞ ♂
Photo: H. Linke

X18115-4 Betta sp. "KUBU"
Sharphead Mouthbrooder   MALE   ADULT
Borneo: Kubu, W, 8 cm

▷ ▯P ◗ ☺ ☺ ⊡ 🖼 🐟 ◈ ⊞ ♂
Photo: G. Kopic

X18115-4 Betta sp. "KUBU"
Sharphead Mouthbrooder   FEMALE   ADULT
Borneo: Kubu, W, 8 cm

▷ ▯P ◗ ☺ ☺ ⊡ 🖼 🐟 ◈ ⊞ ♀
Photo: H. Linke

© Verlag A.C.S. GmbH

X15355-4 Betta enisae KOTTELAT, 1995   MALE

Photo: J. Schmidt

X18125-4 Betta sp. "MANDOR"
Mandor Mouthbrooder   MALE   ADULT
Borneo: Mandor, W, 8 cm

▷ ℙ ◐ ☺ ☹ ⬇ 🕸 ➔: ⚠ 🔲 ♂   Photo: J. Schmidt

X18125-4 Betta sp. "MANDOR"
Mandor Mouthbrooder   FEMALE   ADULT
Borneo: Mandor, W, 8 cm

▷ ℙ ◐ ☺ ☹ ⬇ 🕸 ➔: ⚠ 🔲 ♀   Photo: H. Linke

X18126-4 Betta sp. "MANDOR-4"
Mandor Mouthbrooder Type 4 MALE   ADULT
Borneo: Mandor, W, 8 cm

▷ ℙ ◐ ☺ ☹ ⬇ 🕸 ➔: ⚠ 🔲 ♂   Photo: J. Schmidt

X18127-4 Betta sp. "MANDOR-5"
Mandor Mouthbrooder Type 5 MALE   ADULT
Borneo: Mandor, W, 8 cm

▷ ℙ ◐ ☺ ☹ ⬇ 🕸 ➔: ⚠ 🔲 ♂   Photo: J. Schmidt

X18128-3 Betta sp. "Mantang"
Mantang Mouthbrooder   SUBADULT
Mantang, W, 8 cm (?)

▷ ℙ ◐ ☺ ☹ ⬇ 🕸 ➔: ◈ 🔲   Photo: H. Linke

X15355-4 Betta sp. "NORTHWEST-KALIMANTAN" (= B. enisae)
Blue Band Mouthbrooder   MALE   ADULT
Borneo: Kapuas, W, 8 cm

▷ ℙ ◐ ☺ ☹ ⬇ 🕸 ➔: ◈ 🔲 ♂   Photo: H. Linke

X14616-4 Betta sp. "PALANKANBUN" (= B. burdigala?)
Palankanbun Dwarf Fighter   MALE   ADULT
Borneo, W, 5 cm

▷ ℙ ◐ ☺ ☹ ⬇ 🕸 🐛 ⚠ Ⓢ ♂   Photo: H. Linke

X14616-4 Betta sp. "PALANKANBUN" (= Betta burdigala?)
Palankanbun Dwarf Fighter   FEMALE   ADULT
Borneo, W, 5 cm

▷ ℙ ◐ ☺ ☹ ⬇ 🕸 🐛 ⚠ Ⓢ ♀   Photo: E. Schraml

X18129-4 Betta sp. "PUDUKUALI"
Pudukuali Mouthbrooder　　MALE　　ADULT
Borneo: Pudukuali, W, 8 cm

▷ Ɫ ◐ ☺ ☹ ⬇️ 🔊 ➡️ ⚠️ m ♂　　Photo: H. Linke

X18130-4 Betta sp. "PULAU LAUT" (= sp. aff. patoti)
Pulau Laut Mouthbrooder　　MALE　　ADULT
Pulau Laut island, W, 12 cm

▷ Ɫ ◑ ☺ ☹ ⬇️ 🔊 ➡️ ◈ L ♂　　Photo: H. Linke

X18135-4 Betta sp. "SANGAU"
Sangau Mouthbrooder　　MALE　　ADULT
Borneo: Sangau, W, 8 cm (?)

▷ Ɫ ◐ ☺ ☹ ⬇️ 🔊 ➡️ ◈ m ♂　　Photo: H. Linke

X18136-3 Betta sp. "SKRANG RIVER"
Skrang River Mouthbrooder　　SUBADULT
Borneo: Skrang River, W, 12 cm

▷ Ɫ ◑ ☺ ☹ ⬇️ 🔊 ➡️ ◈ L　　Photo: H. Linke

X18136-4 Betta sp. "SKRANG RIVER"
Skrang River Mouthbrooder　　MALE　　ADULT
Borneo: Skrang River, W, 12 cm

▷ Ɫ ◑ ☺ ☹ ⬇️ 🔊 ➡️ ◈ L ♂　　Photo: H. Linke

X18137-4 Betta sp. "TANGKILING"
Tangkiling Mouthbrooder　　MALE　　ADULT
Borneo: Tangkiling, W, 8 cm

▷ Ɫ ◐ ☺ ☹ ⬇️ 🔊 ➡️ ⚠️ m ♂　　Photo: H. Linke

X18137-4 Betta sp. "TANGKILING"
Tangkiling Mouthbrooder　　FEMALE　　ADULT
Borneo: Tangkiling, W, 8 cm

▷ Ɫ ◐ ☺ ☹ ⬇️ 🔊 ➡️ ⚠️ m ♀　　Photo: H. Linke

X18145-4 Betta sp. "TARANTANG"
Tarantang Mouthbrooder　　FEMALE　　ADULT
Borneo: Tarantang, W, 8 cm

▷ Ɫ ◐ ☺ ☹ ⬇️ 🔊 ➡️ ⚠️ m ♀　　Photo: H. Linke

Photo: J. Vierke

Photo: J. Vierke

Betta climacura: Bei der Paarung in Bodennähe umschlingt das Männchen das Weibchen U-förmig. Die Eier fallen auf die After- oder Schwanzflosse des Männchens, wo sie das Weibchen einsammelt und ins Maul nimmt. Später übergibt sie die Eier dem Männchen zur weiteren Brutpflege (s. Seite 47).

Betta climacura: the pairing is always performed near the ground. The male bends around the female in U-shape during the process. The fertilized eggs are dropped on the male´s anal or caudal fin where they are collected by the female that takes the eggs into her mouth. Later, she passes the eggs on to the male for further brood caring (see page 47).

© Verlag A.C.S. GmbH

X18205-4 Betta spilotogena NG & KOTTELAT, 1994
Double lipspot Mouthbrooder MALE   ADULT
Malaysia: Bintan, W, 13 cm

Photo: P. K. L. Ng

X18205-4 Betta spilotogena NG & KOTTELAT, 1994
Double lipspot Mouthbrooder MALE   ADULT
Malaysia: Bintan, W, 13 cm

Photo: H. Linke

X18305-4 Betta splendens REGAN, 1909
Siamese Fighter, Aquarium Stock   MALE   ADULT
Southeast Asia, B, 6 cm

Photo: B. Teichfischer

X18305-4 Betta splendens REGAN, 1909
Siamese Fighter, Aquarium Stock   FEMALE   ADULT
Southeast Asia, B, 6 cm

Photo: B. Teichfischer

X18305-4 Betta splendens REGAN, 1909
Siamese Fighter   MALE ADULT
Southeast Asia, W, 6 cm

Photo: J. Vierke

X18305-4 Betta splendens REGAN, 1909
Siamese Fighter,   MALE ADULT
Southeast Asia, W, 6 cm

Photo: U. Werner

X18306-4 Betta splendens "BAN PAK BARA"
Siamese Fighter   MALE   ADULT
Thailand: Ban Pak Bara, W, 6 cm

Photo: J. Schmidt

X18307-4 Betta splendens "CHA AM"
Siamese Fighter   MALE   ADULT
Thailand: Cha Am, W, 6 cm

Photo: J. Schmidt

X18308-4 Betta splendens "HUA HIN"
Siamese Fighter　MALE　ADULT
Thailand: Hua Hin, W, 6 cm

▷♫◑☺☹⬇🖼🐛◈🅼♂ Photo: J. Schmidt

X18309-4 Betta splendens "KHAO YAI"
Siamese Fighter　MALE　ADULT
Thailand: Khao Yai, W, 6 cm

▷♫◑☺☹⬇🖼🐛◈🅼♂  Photo: S. Inselmann

X18430-4 Betta splendens "KO SAMUI"
Siamese Fighter　MALE　ADULT
Thailand: Ko Samui island, W, 6 cm

▷♫◑☺☹⬇🖼🐛◈🅼♂ Photo: J. Schmidt

X18466-4 Betta splendens "SAM ROY YOD"
Siamese Fighter　MALE　ADULT
Thailand: Sam Roy Yod, W, 6 cm

▷♫◑☺☹⬇🖼🐛◈🅼♂ Photo: J. Schmidt

X18405-4 Betta splendens "PROFESSIONAL FIGHTER"
Rumble Fish　MALE　ADULT
Southeast Asia, B, 6 cm

▷♫◑☺☹⬇🖼🐛◈🅼♂ Photo: J. Vierke

X18531-5 Betta splendens "FANTAIL"
Siamese Fighter " WHITE-BLUE" MALE ADULT
Southeast Asia, B, 6 cm

▷♫◑☺☹⬇🖼🐛◈🅼♂  Photo: H. Linke

X18505-5 Betta splendens "FANTAIL"
Siamese Fighter "BLUE"　MALE　ADULT
Southeast Asia, B, 6 cm

▷♫◑☺☹⬇🖼🐛◈🅼♂ Photo: H. Linke

X18505-4 Betta splendens "FANTAIL"
Siamese Fighter "BLUE"　FEMALE　ADULT
Southeast Asia, B, 6 cm

▷♫◑☺☹⬇🖼🐛◈🅼♀ Photo: F. Teigler(/
Archiv ACS

X18520-5 Betta splendens "FANTAIL"
Siamese Fighter "RED"   MALE   ADULT
Southeast Asia, B, 6 cm

 Photo: M. Smith

X18520-5 Betta splendens „FANTAIL"
Siamese Fighter "RED"   FEMALE   ADULT
Southeast Asia, B, 6 cm

Photo: M. Smith

X18516-4 Betta splendens "FANTAIL"
Siamese Fighter "TURQUOISE"   MALE   ADULT
Southeast Asia, B, 6 cm

 Photo: E. Schraml

X18516-4 Betta splendens "FANTAIL"
Siamese Fighter "TURQUOISE"   FEMALE   ADULT
Southeast Asia, B, 6 cm

Photo: F. Teigler/
Archiv ACS

X18506-4 Betta splendens "FANTAIL"
Siamese Fighter "VIOLET"   MALE   ADULT
Southeast Asia, B, 6 cm

Photo: F. Teigler/
Archiv ACS

X18506-4 Betta splendens "FANTAIL"
Siamese Fighter "VIOLET"   FEMALE   ADULT
Southeast Asia, B, 6 cm

Photo: F. Teigler/
Archiv ACS

X18515-4 Betta splendens "FANTAIL"
Siamese Fighter "GREEN"   MALE   ADULT
Southeast Asia, B, 6 cm

Photo: F. Teigler/
Archiv ACS

X18515-4 Betta splendens "FANTAIL"
Siamese Fighter "GREEN"   FEMALE   ADULT
Southeast Asia, B, 6 cm

Photo: F. Teigler/
Archiv ACS

X18530-5 Betta splendens "FANTAIL"
Siamese Fighter "WHITE"   MALE   ADULT
Southeast Asia, B, 6 cm
Photo: E. Schraml

X18530-4 Betta splendens "FANTAIL"
Siamese Fighter "WHITE"   FEMALE   ADULT
Southeast Asia, B, 6 cm
Photo: F. Teigler/ Archiv ACS

X18507-5 Betta splendens "FANTAIL"
Siamese Fighter "LIGHTVIOLET"   MALE   ADULT
Southeast Asia, B, 6 cm
Photo: E. Schraml

X18532-4 Betta splendens "FANTAIL"
Siamese Fighter " LIGHTBLUE"   MALE   ADULT
Southeast Asia, B, 6 cm
Photo: F. Teigler/ Archiv ACS

X18525-4 Betta splendens "FANTAIL"
Siamese Fighter "BLACK"   MALE   ADULT
Southeast Asia, B, 6 cm
Photo: J. Vierke

X18330-4 Betta splendens "DOUBLETAIL"
Siamese Fighter " BLACK"   MALE   ADULT
Southeast Asia, B, 6 cm
Photo: J. Vierke

X18335-4 Betta splendens "DOUBLETAIL"
Siamese Fighter "WHITE"   MALE   ADULT
Southeast Asia, B, 6 cm
Photo: J. Vierke

X18335-4 Betta splendens "DOUBLETAIL"
Siamese Fighter "WHITE"   FEMALE   ADULT
Southeast Asia, B, 6 cm
Photo: F. Teigler/ Archiv ACS

© **Verlag A.C.S. GmbH**

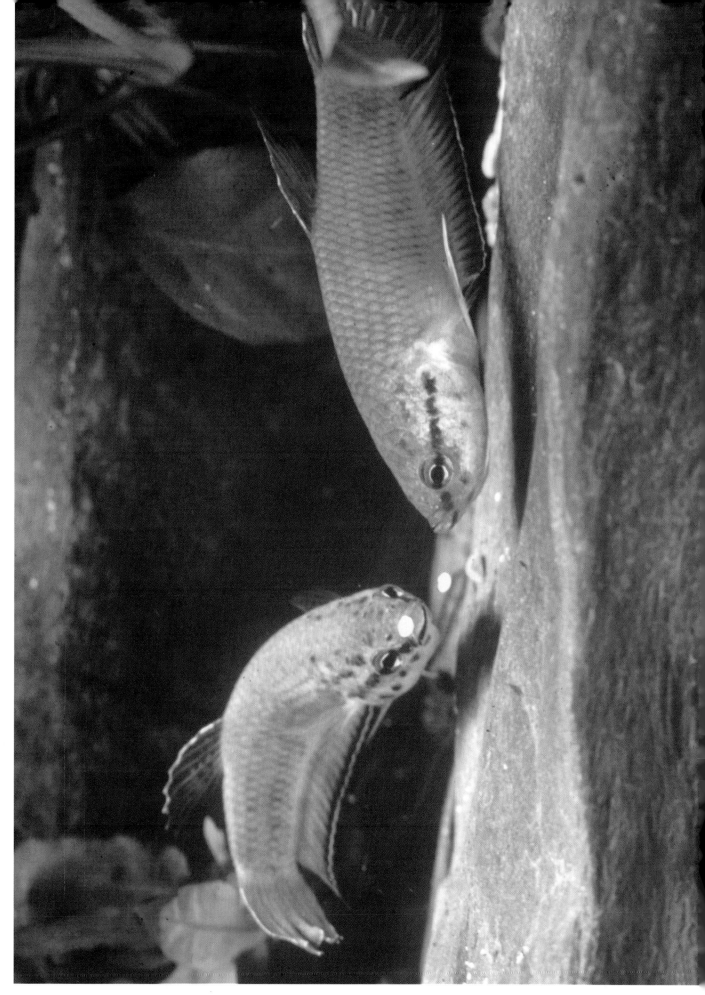

Betta picta: Das Weibchen spuckt dem Männchen die Eier vor das Maul, welches sie zum weiteren Erbrüten in seinem Kehlsack verstaut.

Photo: J. Glaser

Betta picta: The female spits out the eggs in front of the male´s mouth that stores them in his throat for further brooding.

X18310-4 Betta splendens "DOUBLETAIL"
Siamese Fighter "BLUE" FEMALE ADULT
Southeast Asia, B, 6 cm
Photo: F. Teigler/ Archiv ACS

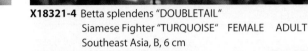

X18321-4 Betta splendens "DOUBLETAIL"
Siamese Fighter "TURQUOISE" FEMALE ADULT
Southeast Asia, B, 6 cm
Photo: F. Teigler/ Archiv ACS

X19105-4 Betta strohi SCHALLER & KOTTELAT, 1989
Father Strohs Mouthbrooder MALE ADULT
Borneo: Kalimantan berah, Kalimantan barat, W, 7 cm
Photo: H. Linke

X19205-4 Betta taeniata REGAN, 1910
Striped Mouthbrooder PAIR ADULT
Borneo: Sarawak, W, 8 cm
Photo: J. Vierke

X19215-4 Betta taeniata "SERIAN"
Striped Mouthbrooder MALE ADULT
Borneo: Sarawak, W, 8 cm
Photo: J. Schmidt

X19215-4 Betta taeniata "SERIAN"
Striped Mouthbrooder FEMALE ADULT
Borneo: Sarawak, W, 8 cm
Photo: J. Schmidt

X19255-4 Betta tomi NG & KOTTELAT, 1994
Tomi Mouthbrooder MALE ADULT
Malaysia: Johore, Singapore, W, 14 cm
Photo: H. Linke

X19255-4 Betta tomi NG & KOTTELAT, 1994
Tomi Mouthbrooder MALE ADULT
Malaysia: Johore, Singapore, W, 14 cm
Photo: P. K. L. Ng

© Verlag A.C.S. GmbH

X19315-4 Betta tussyae SCHALLER, 1985
Tussys Small Red Fighter   MALE   ADULT
E-Malaysia: Pahang (this fish from terra typica), W, 6 cm
Photo: J. Schmidt

X19315-4 Betta tussyae SCHALLER, 1985
Tussys Small Red Fighter   FEMALE   ADULT
E-Malaysia: Pahang (this fish from terra typica), W, 6 cm
Photo: J. Schmidt

X19315-4 Betta tussyae SCHALLER, 1985
Tussys Small Red Fighter   MALE   ADULT
E-Malaysia: Pahang , W, 6 cm
Photo: H. Linke

X19315-4 Betta tussyae SCHALLER, 1985
Tussys Small Red Fighter   FEMALE   ADULT
E-Malaysia: Pahang , W, 6 cm
Photo: H. Linke

X19445-4 Betta unimaculata (POPTA, 1905)
One Spot Mouthbrooder   MALE   ADULT
Borneo: Kalimantan Timur, Sabah, W, 12 cm
Photo: E. Schraml

X19445-4 Betta unimaculata (POPTA, 1905)
One Spot Mouthbrooder   FEMALE   ADULT
Borneo: Kalimantan Timur, Sabah, W, 12 cm
Photo: H. Linke

X19465-4 Betta unimaculata "TAWAU" (= B. ocellata?)
One Spot Mouthbrooder   PAIR   ADULT
Borneo: Sabah (Tawau), W, 12 cm
Photo: J. Schmidt

X19475-4 Betta unimaculata "KAMPONG IMAM"
One Spot Mouthbrooder   MALE   ADULT
Borneo: Sabah (Tawau), W, 12 cm
Photo: J. Schmidt

X40255-5 Colisa lalia "RED"   MALE

Photo: J. Glaser

X40215-5 Colisa lalia "BREEDED"   MALE

Photo: J. Glaser

© Verlag A.C.S. GmbH

X19455-4 Betta unimaculata "BLUE BREEDING-FORM"
Blue One Spot Mouthbrooder   MALE   ADULT
Breeding Form, B, 12 cm

▷ ₽ ◑ ☺ ☻ ⊡ ▦ �']: ◈ ⊡ ♂   Photo: H. Linke

X20005-4 Betta waseri KRUMMENACHER, 1986
Wasers Mouthbrooder   ADULT
Malaysia: Pahang, W, 14 cm

▷ ₽ ◑ ☺ ☻ ⊡ ▦ ➳: ◈ ⊡   Photo: P. K. L. Ng

X20005-3 Betta waseri KRUMMENACHER, 1986
Wasers Mouthbrooder   SUBADULT
Malaysia: Pahang, W, 14 cm

▷ ₽ ◑ ☺ ☻ ⊡ ▦ ➳: ◈ ⊡   Photo: H. Linke

X40005-3 Colisa chuna (HAMILTON-BUCHANAN, 1822) (Syn: C. sota)
Honey Gourami   SUBADULT
India, B, 5 cm

▷ ₽ ◑ ☺ ☻ ⊞ ▦ 🐛 ◈ ⑤   Photo: F. Teigler/
Archiv ACS

X40005-5 Colisa chuna (HAMILTON-BUCHANAN, 1822) (Syn: C. sota)
Honey Gourami   MALE   ADULT
India, B, 5 cm

▷ ₽ ◑ ☺ ☻ ⊞ ▦ 🐛 ◈ ⑤ ♂   Photo: U. Werner

X40005-4 Colisa chuna (HAMILTON-BUCHANAN, 1822) (Syn: C. sota)
Honey Gourami, Breeding colour   PAIR   ADULT
India, B, 5 cm

▷ ₽ ◑ ☺ ☻ ⊞ ▦ 🐛 ◈ ⑤ ♂ ♀   Photo: J. Glaser

X40015-3 Colisa chuna "GOLD"
Golden Honey Gourami   MALE   SUBADULT
Breeding Form, B, 5 cm

▷ ₽ ◑ ☺ ☻ ⊞ ▦ 🐛 ◈ ⑤ ♂   Photo: F. Teigler/
Archiv ACS

X40015-3 Colisa chuna "GOLD"
Golden Honey Gourami   FEMALE   SUBADULT
Breeding Form, B, 5 cm

▷ ₽ ◑ ☺ ☻ ⊞ ▦ 🐛 ◈ ⑤ ♀   Photo: F. Teigler/
Archiv ACS

X40015-4 Colisa chuna "GOLD"
Golden Honey Gourami   MALE   ADULT
Breeding Form, B, 5 cm

▷ 🏷 ◐ ☺ ☹ ⊞ 🖼 🦎 ◈ Ⓢ ♂   Photo: J. Glaser

X40015-4 Colisa chuna "GOLD"
Golden Honey Gourami   FEMALE   ADULT
Breeding Form, B, 5 cm

▷ 🏷 ◐ ☺ ☹ ⊞ 🖼 🦎 ◈ Ⓢ ♀   Photo: J. Glaser

X40115-5 Colisa fasciata (BLOCH & SCHNEIDER, 1801)
Striped Gourami   PAIR   ADULT
India, W, 12 cm

▷ 🏷 ◐ ☺ ☹ ⊞ 🖼 🦎 ◈ Ⓜ ♂ ♀   Photo: F. Teigler/ Archiv ACS

X40116-5 Colisa fasciata (BLOCH & SCHNEIDER, 1801)
Striped Gourami   MALE   ADULT
India, B, 12 cm

▷ 🏷 ◐ ☺ ☹ ⊞ 🖼 🦎 ◈ Ⓜ ♂   Photo: J. Vierke

X40116-4 Colisa fasciata (BLOCH & SCHNEIDER, 1801)
Striped Gourami   MALE   ADULT
India, B, 12 cm

▷ 🏷 ◐ ☺ ☹ ⊞ 🖼 🦎 ◈ Ⓜ ♂   Photo: F. Teigler/ Archiv ACS

X40116-4 Colisa fasciata (BLOCH & SCHNEIDER, 1801)
Striped Gourami   FEMALE   ADULT
India, B, 12 cm

▷ 🏷 ◐ ☺ ☹ ⊞ 🖼 🦎 ◈ Ⓜ ♀   Photo: F. Teigler/ Archiv ACS

X40155-4 Colisa labiosa (DAY, 1878)
Thicklip Gourami   MALE   ADULT
Birma, B, 10 cm

▷ 🏷 ◐ ☺ ☹ ⊞ 🖼 🦎 ◈ Ⓜ ♂   Photo: Archiv ACS Migge/ Reinhard

X40155-4 Colisa labiosa (DAY, 1878)
Thicklip Gourami   FEMALE   ADULT
Birma, B, 10 cm

▷ 🏷 ◐ ☺ ☹ ⊞ 🖼 🦎 ◈ Ⓜ ♀   Photo: J. Glaser

X40165-4 Colisa labiosa "PEACH"
Peach Gourami   MALE   ADULT
Breeding Form, B, 10 cm

 Photo: M. Smith

X40165-4 Colisa labiosa "PEACH"
Peach Gourami   FEMALE   ADULT
Breeding Form, B, 10 cm

Photo: F. Teigler/
Archiv ACS

X40205-5 Colisa Hybrid (wildcaught between wild C. lalia)
Crossbred Gourami   SUBADULT
India, W, 6 cm (?)

 Photo: F. Teigler/
Archiv ACS

X40206-5 Colisa Hybrid C. lalia x C. labiosa
Crossbred Gourami II   MALE   ADULT
Breeding Form, B, 7 cm

Photo: J. Vierke

X 40275-4 Colisa lalia (HAMILTON-BUCHANAN, 1822)
Wild Dwarf Gourami   PAIR   ADULT
India, W, 6 cm

Photo: F. Teigler/
Archiv ACS

X40215-5 Colisa lalia (HAMILTON-BUCHANAN, 1822)
Dwarf Gourami   MALE   ADULT
India, B, 6 cm

Photo: Archiv ACS
Migge/ Reinhard

X40216-4 Colisa lalia "BLUE"
Blue Dwarf Gourami   MALE   ADULT
Breeding Form, B, 6 cm

 Photo: M. Smith

X40245-5 Colisa lalia "RAINBOW"
Rainbow Dwarf Gourami   MALE   ADULT
Breeding Form, B, 6 cm

Photo: J. Vierke

X40155-5 Colisa labiosa   MALE   Breeding colour

Photo: J. Glaser

© Verlag A.C.S. GmbH

1. Aphanius mento
2. Aphyosemion monroviae

Diese und alle anderen in
These and all other in

all Killis of the old world I

reference fish of the world

X40255-4 Colisa lailia "RED"
Red Dwarf Gourami   PAIR   ADULT
Breeding Form, B, 6 cm

Photo: F. Teigler/ Archiv ACS

X 40235-4 Colisa lalia "MULTICOLOURED"
Multicoloured Dwarf Gourami Var. I   MALE   ADULT
Breeding Form, B, 6 cm

Photo: U. Werner

X40236-4 Colisa lalia "MULTICOLOURED"
Multicoloured Dwarf Gourami Var. II   MALE   ADULT
Breeding Form, B, 6 cm

Photo: U. Werner

X40237-4 Colisa lalia "MULTICOLOURED"
Multicoloured Dwarf Gourami Var. III   MALE   ADULT
Breeding Form, B, 6 cm

Photo: U. Werner

X40225-4 Colisa lalia "NEON"
Neon Dwarf Gourami   MALE   ADULT
Breeding Form, B, 6 cm

Photo: F. Teigler/ Archiv ACS

X40225-4 Colisa lalia "NEON"
Neon Dwarf Gourami   FEMALE   ADULT
Breeding Form, B, 6 cm

Photo: F. Teigler/ Archiv ACS

A25445-4 Ctenopoma acutirostre (PELLEGRIN, 1899)
Leopard Bushfish   ADULT
Kongo Bassin: Leopoldville, W, 20 cm

Photo: F. Teigler/ Archiv ACS

A25441-3 Ctenopoma acutirostre (PELLEGRIN, 1899)
Leopard Bushfish unspotted variety MALE   SUBADULT
Kongo Bassin: Leopoldville, W, 20 cm

Photo: F. Teigler/ Archiv ACS

© Verlag A.C.S. GmbH

A25442-4 Ctenopoma acutirostre "VIOLET"
Violet Leopard Bushfish   MALE   ADULT
Zaire: commercial import, W, 15 cm

▷ ⤳ ₿ ◐ ☺ ☻ ⊞ 🖼 ➤ ◈ ⊞ ♂   Photo: F. Schäfer

A25442-4 Ctenopoma acutirostre "VIOLET"
Violet Leopard Bushfish   FEMALE   ADULT
Zaire: commercial import, W, 15 cm

▷ ⤳ ₿ ◐ ☺ ☻ ⊞ 🖼 ➤ ◈ ⊞ ♀   Photo: F. Schäfer

A25450-4 Ctenopoma ansorgii (BOULENGER, 1912)
Orange Bushfish   MALE   ADULT
Zaire river bassin, W, 8 cm

◁ ⵊP ◐ ☺ ☻ ⊞ 🖼 🐛 ⚠ ⊞ ♂   Photo: F. Teigler/
Archiv ACS

A25450-4 Ctenopoma ansorgii (BOULENGER, 1912)
Orange Bushfish   FEMALE   ADULT
Zaire river bassin, W, 8 cm

◁ ⵊP ◐ ☺ ☻ ⊞ 🖼 🐛 ⚠ ⊞ ♀   Photo: F. Teigler/
Archiv ACS

A25451-4 Ctenopoma ansorgii (BOULENGER, 1912)
Orange Bushfish Var. I   MALE   ADULT
Zaire river bassin, W, 8 cm

◁ ⵊP ◐ ☺ ☻ ⊞ 🖼 🐛 ⚠ ⊞ ♂   Photo: E. Pürzl

A25452-4 Ctenopoma ansorgii (BOULENGER, 1912)
Orange Bushfish Var.II   MALE   ADULT
Zaire river bassin, W, 8 cm

◁ ⵊP ◐ ☺ ☻ ⊞ 🖼 🐛 ⚠ ⊞ ♂   Photo: U. Werner

A25460-5 Ctenopoma congicum BOULENGER, 1887
Congo Bushfish   MALE   ADULT
Central African Republic: Kampon, W, 8 cm

◁ ⵊP ◐ ☺ ☻ ⊞ 🖼 🐛 ⚠ ⊞ ♂   Photo: S. Inselmann

A25460-5 Ctenopoma congicum BOULENGER, 1887
Congo Bushfish   FEMALE   ADULT
Central African Republic: Kampon, W, 8 cm

◁ ⵊP ◐ ☺ ☻ ⊞ 🖼 🐛 ⚠ ⊞ ♀   Photo: S. Inselmann

A25461-4 Ctenopoma sp. aff. congicum (C. multifasciatum PLG.?)
Multiband Bushfish   MALE   ADULT
Lualaba-River, W, 8 cm
◁ ℙ ◕ ☺ ☻ ⊞ 🖼 🐛 ⚠ ⊞ ♂
Photo: H. Linke

A25464-3 Ctenopoma damasi (POLL, 1939)
Pearl Bushfish   MALE   SUBADULT
E-Uganda, W, 8 cm
◁ ℙ ◕ ☺ ☻ ⊞ 🖼 🐛 ⚠ ⊞ ♂
Photo: H.-G. Evers

A25464-4 Ctenopoma damasi (POLL, 1939)
Pearl Bushfish   MALE   ADULT
E-Uganda, W, 8 cm
◁ ℙ ◕ ☺ ☻ ⊞ 🖼 🐛 ⚠ ⊞ ♂
Photo: J. Vierke

A25463-4 Ctenopoma damasi (POLL, 1939)
Pearl Bushfish Var.I   MALE   ADULT
E-Uganda, W, 8 cm
◁ ℙ ◕ ☺ ☻ ⊞ 🖼 🐛 ⚠ ⊞ ♂
Photo: L. Seegers

A25463-4 Ctenopoma damasi (POLL, 1939)
Pearl Bushfish Var.I   FEMALE   ADULT
E-Uganda, W, 8 cm
◁ ℙ ◕ ☺ ☻ ⊞ 🖼 🐛 ⚠ ⊞ ♀
Photo: L. Seegers

A25466-4 Ctenopoma fasciolatum (BOULENGER, 1899)
Banded Bushfish Form A   MALE   ADULT
Zaire: commercial import, W, 8 cm
◁ ℙ ◕ ☺ ☻ ⊞ 🖼 🐛 ◇ ⊞ ♂
Photo: J. Vierke

A25467-4 Ctenopoma fasciolatum (BOULENGER, 1899)
Banded Bushfish Form B (blue)   MALE ADULT
Zaire: commercial import, W, 8 cm
◁ ℙ ◕ ☺ ☻ ⊞ 🖼 🐛 ◇ ⊞ ♂
Photo: F. Teigler/
Archiv ACS

A25467-5 Ctenopoma fasciolatum (BOULENGER, 1899)
Banded Bushfish Form B (blue)   MALE ADULT
Zaire: commercial import, W, 8 cm
◁ ℙ ◕ ☺ ☻ ⊞ 🖼 🐛 ◇ ⊞ ♂
Photo: J. Vierke

A25452-5 Ctenopoma ansorgii   Two fighting males

Photo: U. Werner

A25475-5 Ctenopoma kingsleyae

Photo: A. Canovas

A25468-4 Ctenopoma fasciolatum (BOULENGER, 1899)
Banded Bushfish Form C (brown)   MALE   ADULT
Zaire: commercial import, W, 8 cm
◁ ℗ ◕ ☺ ☹ ⊞ 🖼 🦎 ◈ 🔟 ♂   Photo: F. Teigler/ Archiv ACS

A25468-4 Ctenopoma fasciolatum (BOULENGER, 1899)
Banded Bushfish Form C (brown)   FEMALE ADULT
Zaire: commercial import, W, 8 cm
◁ ℗ ◕ ☺ ☹ ⊞ 🖼 🦎 ◈ 🔟 ♀   Photo: F. Teigler/ Archiv ACS

A25467-4 Ctenopoma fasciolatum (BOULENGER, 1899)
Banded Bushfish Form B (blue)   MALE   ADULT
Zaire, W, 8 cm
◁ ℗ ◕ ☺ ☹ ⊞ 🖼 🦎 ◈ 🔟 ♂   Photo: L. Seegers

A25468-4 Ctenopoma fasciolatum (BOULENGER, 1899)
Banded Bushfish Form C(brown)   MALE   ADULT
Zaire: Boma, W, 8 cm
◁ ℗ ◕ ☺ ☹ ⊞ 🖼 🦎 ◈ 🔟 ♂   Photo: E. Pürzl

A25470-4 Ctenopoma cf. intermedium
Pale Bushfish   MALE   ADULT
Zaire: Kindu, W, 8 cm
◁ ℗ ◕ ☺ ☹ ⊞ 🖼 🦎 ⚠ 🔟 ♂   Photo: L. Seegers

A25475-2 Ctenopoma kingsleyae GÜNTHER, 1896
Tailspot Bushfish   JUVENIL
West-Africa: commercial import, W, 20 cm
▷ ₿ ◑ ☺ ☹ ⊞ 🖼 🐛 ◈ 🔟   Photo: F. Schäfer

A25475-3 Ctenopoma kingsleyae GÜNTHER, 1896
Tailspot Bushfish   SUBADULT
West-Africa: commercial import, W, 20 cm
▷ ₿ ◑ ☺ ☹ ⊞ 🖼 🐛 ◈ 🔟   Photo: Archiv ACS H.-J. Mayland

A25475-5 Ctenopoma kingsleyae GÜNTHER, 1896
Tailspot Bushfish   PAIR   ADULT
West-Africa: commercial import, W, 20 cm
▷ ₿ ◑ ☺ ☹ ⊞ 🖼 🐛 ◈ 🔟 ♂ ♀   Photo: F. Schäfer

© **Verlag A.C.S. GmbH**

A25476-4 Ctenopoma kingsleyae GÜNTHER, 1896
Tailspot Bushfish Form A   FEMALE   ADULT
Zaire: commercial import, W, 20 cm

▷ ₽ ◑ ☺ ☻ ⊞ 🖼 ➽ ◈ 🔲 ♀   Photo: F. Teigler/ Archiv ACS

A25477-4 Ctenopoma kingsleyae GÜNTHER, 1896
Tailspot Bushfish Form B   MALE   ADULT
West Africa: commercial import, W, 20 cm

▷ ₽ ◑ ☺ ☻ ⊞ 🖼 ➽ ◈ 🔲 ♂   Photo: U. Werner

A25479-4 Ctenopoma kingsleyae (= C. argentoventer)
Tailspot Bushfish Form C   MALE   ADULT
West-Africa: commercial import, W, 20 cm

▷ ₽ ◑ ☺ ☻ ⊞ 🖼 ➽ ◈ 🔲 ♂   Photo: F. Schäfer

A25479-4 Ctenopoma kingsleyae (= C. argentoventer)
Tailspot Bushfish Form C   FEMALE ADULT
West-Africa: commercial import, W, 20 cm

▷ ₽ ◑ ☺ ☻ ⊞ 🖼 ➽ ◈ 🔲 ♀   Photo: F. Schäfer

A25480-4 Ctenopoma kingsleyae GÜNTHER, 1896
Tailspot Bushfish Form D   MALE   ADULT
Ivory Coast: Bounua, W, 20 cm

▷ ₽ ◑ ☺ ☻ ⊞ 🖼 ➽ ◈ 🔲 ♂   Photo:E. Pürzl

A25483-4 Ctenopoma maculatum THOMINOT, 1886
Single Spotted Bushfish   ADULT
S-Cameroon, W, 15 cm

◁ ₽ ◑ ☺ ☻ ⊞ 🖼 ➽ ◈ 🔲   Photo: Archiv ACS H.-J. Mayland

A25483-4 Ctenopoma maculatum THOMINOT, 1886
Single Spotted Bushfish   ADULT
S-Cameroon, W, 15 cm

◁ ₽ ◑ ☺ ☻ ⊞ 🖼 ➽ ◈ 🔲   Photo: Archiv ACS H.-J. Mayland

A25486-2 Ctenopoma multispinis PETERS, 1844
Many Spined Bushfish   JUVENIL
Zambia, W, 15 cm

▷ ₽ ◑ ☺ ☻ ⊞ 🖼 ➽ ◈ 🔲   Photo: L. Seegers

A25486-4 Ctenopoma multispinis PETERS, 1844
Many Spined Bushfish ADULT
South of Africa, W, 15 cm

Photo: H. Linke

A25489-4 Ctenopoma muriei (BOULENGER, 1896)
Small Tailspot Bushfish ADULT
Uganda, W, 10 cm

Photo: U. Renninger

A25489-3 Ctenopoma muriei (BOULENGER, 1896)
Small Tailspot Bushfish SUBADULT
Uganda, W, 10 cm

Photo: L. Seegers

A25491-5 Ctenopoma muriei (BOULENGER, 1896)(Syn: C. ctenotis)
Small Tailspot Bushfish ADULT
W-Uganda, W, 10 cm

Photo: M. Smith

A25490-4 Ctenopoma muriei (BOULENGER, 1896)
Small Tailspot Bushfish ADULT
Tanzania, W, 10 cm

Photo. L. Seegers

A25488-2 Ctenopoma sp. aff. muriei
Similar Small Tailspot Bushfish JUVENIL
Tanzania, W, 10 cm

Photo: L. Seegers

A25488-3 Ctenopoma sp. aff. muriei
Similar Small Tailspot Bushfish SUBADULT
Tanzania, W, 10 cm

Photo: L. Seegers

A25495-3 Ctenopoma nanum GÜNTHER, 1896
Dwarf Bushfish MALE SUBADULT
Cameroon, Gaboon, Zaire, W, 8 cm

Photo: H. Linke

© Verlag A.C.S. GmbH

A25495-4 Ctenopoma nanum GÜNTHER, 1896
Dwarf Bushfish   MALE   ADULT
Cameroon, Gaboon, Zaire, W, 8 cm
◁ ⼘🅟●☺☺🎛🖼🦖 ⚠️🔳 ♂
Photo: J. Vierke

A25498-2 Ctenopoma nebulosum NORRIS, 1990
Fog Bushfish   JUVENIL
Calabar, W, 15 cm
▷🅡◑☺☺🎛🖼🐟 ◈🔳
Photo: H. Linke

A25498-4 Ctenopoma nebulosum NORRIS, 1990
Fog Bushfish   ADULT
SE-Nigeria, W, 15 cm
▷🅡◑☺☺🎛🖼🐟 ◈🔳
Photo: H. Linke

A25500-4 Ctenopoma cf. nigropannosum
Dark Bushfish   ADULT
West-Africa (origin of this fish unknown), W, 15 cm
▷🅡◑☺☺🎛🖼🐟 ◈🔳
Photo: E. Schraml

A25504-4 Ctenopoma ocellatum (PELLEGRIN, 1899)
Eye Spot Bushfish   ADULT
Zaire: commercial import, W, 15 cm
▷🅡◑☺☺🎛🖼🐟 ◈🔳
Photo: F. Teigler/
Archiv ACS

A25516-4 Ctenopoma cf. ocellatum
Brown Eye Spot Bushfish   ADULT
Zaire: commercial import, W, 15 cm
▷🅡◑☺☺🎛🖼🐟 ◈🔳
Photo: E. Schraml

A25515-5 Ctenopoma pellegrini (BOULENGER, 1902)
Pellegrins Bushfish   MALE   ADULT
N-Zaire, W, 15 cm
▷🅡◑☺☺🎛🖼🐟 ◈🔳 ♂
Photo: H. Linke

A25515-5 Ctenopoma pellegrini (BOULENGER, 1902)
Pellegrins Bushfish   FEMALE   ADULT
N-Zaire, W, 15 cm
▷🅡◑☺☺🎛🖼🐟 ◈🔳 ♀
Photo: S. Inselmann

A25515-4 Ctenopoma pellegrini

Photo: L. Seegers

© Verlag A.C.S. GmbH

X42305-4 Ctenops nobilis

Photo: A. Canovas

A25517-4 Ctenopoma petherici GÜNTHER, 1864
Petherics Bushfish   MALE   ADULT
White Nile, Lake Chad, Ivory Coast, parts of W-Africa, W, 16 cm
▷ ♫ ◑ ☺ ☹ ⊞ 🖼 ➡ ◈ 🔲 ♂   Photo: F. Schäfer

A25517-4 Ctenopoma petherici GÜNTHER, 1864
Petherics Bushfish   FEMALE   ADULT
White Nile, Lake Chad, Ivory Coast, parts of W-Africa, W, 16 cm
▷ ♫ ◑ ☺ ☹ ⊞ 🖼 ➡ ◈ 🔲 ♀   Photo: F. Schäfer

A25518-4 Ctenopoma petherici GÜNTHER, 1864
Petherics Bushfish   MALE   ADULT
White Nile, Lake Chad, Ivory Coast, parts of W-Africa, B, 16 cm
▷ ♫ ◑ ☺ ☹ ⊞ 🖼 ➡ ◈ 🔲 ♂   Photo: F. Teigler/
                                            Archiv ACS

A25517-4 Ctenopoma petherici GÜNTHER, 1864
Petherics Bushfish   PAIR   ADULT
White Nile, Lake Chad, Ivory Coast, parts of W-Africa, W, 16 cm
▷ ♫ ◑ ☺ ☹ ⊞ 🖼 ➡ ◈ 🔲 ♂ ♀   Photo: F. Schäfer

A25492-3 Ctenopoma sp. "NTEM"
Ntem Dwarf Bushfish   MALE   SUBADULT
W- Africa: Ntem, W, 8 cm
◁ � ◐ ☺ ☹ ⊞ 🖼 🦎 ⚠ 🔲 ♂   Photo: J. Pinhard/
                                            Archiv ACS

A25492-3 Ctenopoma sp. "NTEM"
Ntem Dwarf Bushfish   FEMALE   SUBADULT
W- Africa: Ntem, W, 8 cm
◁ 112 ◐ ☺ ☹ ⊞ 🖼 🦎 ⚠ 🔲 ♀   Photo: J. Pinhard/
                                            Archiv ACS

A25473-4 Ctenopoma sp. aff. nanum
Gaboon Dwarf Bushfish   MALE   ADULT
W-Africa: Gaboon, Franceville, W, 8 cm
◁ 112 ◐ ☺ ☹ ⊞ 🖼 🦎 ⚠ 🔲 ♂   Photo: E. Pürzl

A25473-4 Ctenopoma sp. aff. nanum
Gaboon Dwarf Bushfish   FEMALE   ADULT
W-Africa: Gaboon, Franceville, W, 8 cm
◁ 112 ◐ ☺ ☹ ⊞ 🖼 🦎 ⚠ 🔲 ♀   Photo: E. Pürzl

A25525-2 Ctenopoma weeksii (BOULENGER, 1896)
Mottled Bushfish   BABY   Synonym: C. oxyrhynchum!
W-Africa: Zaire, W, 12 cm

   Photo: U. Werner

A25525-3 Ctenopoma weeksii (BOULENGER, 1896)
Mottled Bushfish SUBADULT Synonym: C. oxyrhynchum
W-Africa: Zaire, W, 12 cm

Photo: F. Teigler/ Archiv ACS

A25525-4 Ctenopoma weeksii (BOULENGER, 1896)
Mottled Bushfish   MALE   Synonym: C. oxyrhynchum
W-Africa: Zaire, W, 12 cm

Photo: U. Werner

A25525-4 Ctenopoma weeksii (BOULENGER, 1896)
Mottled Bushfish   FEMALE   Synonym: C. oxyrhynchum
W-Africa: Zaire, W, 12 cm

Photo: F. Teigler/ Archiv ACS

A25526-4 Ctenopoma sp. aff. weeksii
Suspect Bushfish   MALE   ADULT
W-Africa: commercial import, W, 10 cm

Photo: F. Teigler/ Archiv ACS

A25526-4 Ctenopoma sp. aff. weeksii
Suspect Bushfish   FEMALE   ADULT
W-Africa: commercial import, W, 10 cm

Photo: F. Teigler/ Archiv ACS

X42305-3 Ctenops nobilis McCLELLAND, 1845
Indian Gourami   SUBADULT
India, W, 12 cm

Photo: F. Teigler/ Archiv ACS

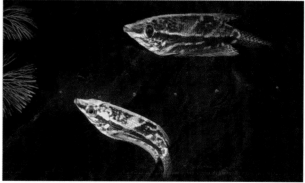

X42305-4 Ctenops nobilis McCLELLAND, 1845
Indian Gourami   ADULT
India, W, 12 cm

Photo: F. Teigler/ Archiv ACS

X42305-4 Ctenops nobilis McCLELLAND, 1845
Indian Gourami ADULT
India, W, 12 cm
Photo: F. Teigler/ Archiv ACS

X42305-4 Ctenops nobilis McCLELLAND, 1845
Indian Gourami ADULT
India, W, 12 cm
Photo: F. Schäfer

X51015-3 Helostoma temminckii (CUVIER & VALENCIENNES, 1831)
Green Kissing Gourami SUBADULT
SE-Asia, W, 30 cm
Photo: F. Teigler/ Archiv ACS

X51015-4 Helostoma temminckii (CUVIER & VALENCIENNES, 1831)
Green Kissing Gourami ADULT
SE-Asia, W, 30 cm
Photo: E. Schraml

X51020-3 Helostoma temminckii (Synonym: H. rudolfi)
Kissing Gourami SUBADULT
SE-Asia, B, 30 cm
Photo: F. Teigler/ Archiv ACS

X51020-4 Helostoma temminckii (Synonym: H. rudolfi)
Kissing Gourami ADULT
SE-Asia, B, 30 cm
Photo: M. Smith

X51020-5 Helostoma temminckii (Synonym: H. rudolfi)
Kissing Gourami ADULT
SE-Asia, B, 30 cm
Photo: B. Teichfischer

X51020-5 Helostoma temminckii (Synonym: H. rudolfi)
Kissing Gourami ADULT
SE-Asia, B, 30 cm
Photo: B. Teichfischer

X51015-3 Helostoma temminckii   FIGHTING

Photo: J. Schmidt

X69555-5 Osphromenus gorami

Photo: U. Werner

© Verlag A.C.S. GmbH

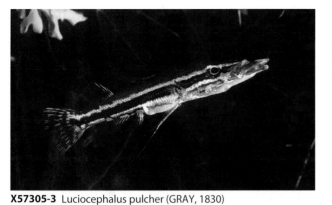

X57305-3 Luciocephalus pulcher (GRAY, 1830)
Pikehead   SUBADULT
Malaysia, Indonesia, W, 20 cm
⚠ℙ◐⊗⬆🔲➤ ⚠🔲   Photo: J. Schmidt

X57305-3 Luciocephalus pulcher (GRAY, 1830)
Pikehead   SUBADULT
Malaysia: Johore, W, 20 cm
⚠ℙ◐⊗⬆🔲➤ ⚠🔲   Photo: P. K. L. Ng

X57305-4 Luciocephalus pulcher (GRAY, 1830)
Pikehead   ADULT
Malaysia, Indonesia, W, 20 cm
⚠ℙ◐⊗⬆🔲➤ ⚠🔲   Photo: Archiv ACS
                                          Migge/Reinhard

X57305-4 Luciocephalus pulcher (GRAY, 1830)
Pikehead   ADULT
Malaysia, W, 20 cm
⚠ℙ◐⊗⬆🔲➤ ⚠🔲   Photo: G. Kopic

X57306-4 Luciocephalus sp. (undescribed species)
Spotted Pikehead   ADULT
Borneo (?), W, 20 cm
⚠ℙ◐⊗⬆🔲➤ ⚠🔲   Photo: M. Kottelat

X58055-4 Macropodus concolor AHL, 1937
Black Paradise Fish   MALE   ADULT
Cambodia, Vietnam (?), B, 12 cm
▷♪◑☺😀➕🔲🦐 ◈🔲♂   Photo: U. werner

X58055-4 Macropodus concolor AHL, 1937
Black Paradise Fish   FEMALE   ADULT
Cambodia, Vietnam (?), B, 12 cm
▷♪◑☺😀➕🔲🦐 ◈🔲♀   Photo: J. Schmidt

X58055-5 Macropodus concolor AHL, 1937
Black Paradise Fish   MALE   ADULT
Cambodia, Vietnam (?), B, 12 cm
▷♪◑☺😀➕🔲🦐 ◈🔲♂   Photo: J. Vierke

X58255-4 Macropodus ocellatus CANTOR, 1842 (Syn: M. chinensis)
Chinese Paradise Fish   MALE   ADULT
China, W, 8 cm

▷ ♬ ◑ ☺ ☹ ⊞ 🐟 🦎 ⚠ m ♂

Photo: F. Teigler/
Archiv ACS

X58255-4 Macropodus ocellatus CANTOR, 1842 (Syn: M. chinensis)
Chinese Paradise Fish   MALE   ADULT
China, W, 8 cm

▷ ♬ ◑ ☺ ☹ ⊞ 🐟 🦎 ⚠ m ♀ ·

Photo: F. Teigler/
Archiv ACS

X58256-5 Macropodus ocellatus CANTOR, 1842 (Syn: M. chinensis)
Chinese Paradise Fish   MALE   ADULT
China, B, 8 cm

▷ ♬ ◑ ☺ ☹ ⊞ 🐟 🦎 ⚠ m ♂

Photo: H. Linke

X58256-4 Macropodus ocellatus CANTOR, 1842 (Syn: M. chinensis)
Chinese Paradise Fish   MALE   ADULT
China, B, 8 cm

▷ ♬ ◑ ☺ ☹ ⊞ 🐟 🦎 ⚠ m ♂

Photo: H.-J. Mayland

X58205-4 Macropodus opercularis x ocellatus
Mattes Paradise Fish   MALE   ADULT
Breeding Form, X, 10 cm

▷ ♬ ◑ ☺ ☹ ⊞ 🐟 🦎 ◈ m ♂

Photo: J. Schmidt

X58105-5 Macropodus opercularis x concolor
Dark Paradise Fish   MALE   ADULT
Breeding Form, X, 12 cm

▷ ♬ ◑ ☺ ☹ ⊞ 🐟 🦎 ◈ m ♂

Photo: B. Teichfischer

X58305-3 Macropodus opercularis (LINNE, 1758)
Paradise Fish   MALE   SUBADULT
S-China, B, 12 cm

▷ ♬ ◑ ☺ ☹ ⊞ 🐟 🦎 ◈ m ♂

Photo: F. Teigler/
Archiv ACS

X58305-3 Macropodus opercularis (LINNE, 1758)
Paradise Fish   FEMALE   SUBADULT
S-China, B, 12 cm

▷ ♬ ◑ ☺ ☹ ⊞ 🐟 🦎 ◈ m ♀

Photo: F. Teigler/
Archiv ACS

© Verlag A.C.S. GmbH

X58305-5 Macropodus opercularis (LINNE, 1758)
Paradise Fish MALE ADULT
S-China, B, 12 cm
Photo: U. Werner

X58305-5 Macropodus opercularis (LINNE, 1758)
Paradise Fish FEMALE ADULT
S-China, B, 12 cm
Photo: F. Schäfer

X58405-4 Macropodus opercularis "BLUE"
Blue Paradise Fish MALE ADULT
Breeding Form, B, 12 cm
Photo: J. Glaser

X58405-4 Macropodus opercularis "BLUE"
Blue Paradise Fish FEMALE ADULT
Breeding Form, B, 12 cm
Photo: F. Teigler/ Archiv ACS

X58355-4 Macropodus opercularis "ALBINO"
Albino Paradise Fish MALE ADULT
Breeding Form, B, 12 cm
Photo: F. Teigler/ Archiv ACS

X58355-4 Macropodus opercularis "ALBINO"
Albino Paradise Fish FEMALE ADULT
Breeding Form, B, 12 cm
Photo: F. Teigler/ Archiv ACS

X59005-2 Malpulutta kretseri DERANIYAGALA, 1937
Ornate Gourami JUVENIL
SriLanka, W, 6 cm
Photo: H.-G. Evers

X59015-4 Malpulutta kretseri minor DERANIYAGALA, 1958
Ornate Gourami MALE ADULT
SriLanka, W, 6 cm
Photo: H. Linke

X59015-4 Malpulutta kretseri minor DERANIYAGALA, 1958
Ornate Gourami   MALE   ADULT
SriLanka: Kottawa forest, W, 6 cm

▷ ℙ ◐ ☺ ☹ ⬇ 🖼 🐛 🐟 ⚠ Ⓢ ♂

Photo: J. Schmidt

X59015-4 Malpulutta kretseri minor DERANIYAGALA, 1958
Ornate Gourami   FEMALE ADULT
SriLanka: Kottawa forest, W, 6 cm

▷ ℙ ◐ ☺ ☹ ⬇ 🖼 🐛 🐟 ⚠ Ⓢ ♀

Photo: J. Schmidt

X59016-4 Malpulutta kretseri "VIOLET"
Violet Ornate Gourami   MALE   ADULT
SriLanka, B, 6 cm

▷ ℙ ◐ ☺ ☹ ⬇ 🖼 🐛 🐟 ⚠ Ⓢ ♂

Photo: J. Schmidt

X59015-5 Malpulutta kretseri minor DERANIYAGALA, 1958
Ornate Gourami   MALE   ADULT
SriLanka: Kottawa forest, W, 6 cm

▷ ℙ ◐ ☺ ☹ ⬇ 🖼 🐛 🐟 ⚠ Ⓢ ♂

Photo: H.-J. Günther

Breeding Station for Osphromenus gorami

Photo: F. Schäfer

X69555-2 Osphromenus gorami LACEPEDE, 1801
Giant Gourami   JUVENIL
Tropical Asia, B, 60 cm

▷ ฿ ◐ ☺ ☹ ⊞ 🖼 🐛 ◈ 🗓

Photo: F. Schäfer

X69555-3 Osphromenus gorami LACEPEDE, 1801
Giant Gourami   SUBADULT
Tropical Asia, B, 60 cm

▷ ฿ ◐ ☺ ☹ ⊞ 🖼 🐛 ◈ 🗓

Photo: Archiv ACS
Migge/Reinhard

X69555-3 Osphromenus gorami LACEPEDE, 1801
Giant Gourami   SUBADULT
Tropical Asia, B, 60 cm

▷ ฿ ◐ ☺ ☹ ⊞ 🖼 🐛 ◈ 🗓

Photo: F. Schäfer

© **Verlag A.C.S. GmbH**

X69555-3 Osphromenus gorami LACEPEDE, 1801
Giant Gourami   SUBADULT
Tropical Asia, B, 60 cm

▷ ♬ ◑ ☺ 😁 ⊞ 🖼 🐾 ◈ 🔠

Photo: F. Teigler/
Archiv ACS

X69555-5 Osphromenus gorami LACEPEDE, 1801
Giant Gourami   ADULT
Tropical Asia, B, 60 cm

▷ ♬ ◑ ☺ 😁 ⊞ 🖼 🐾 ◈ 🔠

Photo: Archiv ACS
Migge/Reinhard

X69556-5 Osphromenus cf. gorami
Orangehead Giant Gourami   MALE   ADULT
Origin unknown, W, 60 cm

▷ ♬ ◑ ☺ 😁 ⊞ 🖼 🐾 ◈ 🔠

Photo: E. Schraml

X69556-5 Osphromenus cf. gorami
Orangehead Giant Gourami   FEMALE   ADULT
Origin unknown, W, 60 cm

▷ ♬ ◑ ☺ 😁 ⊞ 🖼 🐾 ◈ 🔠

Photo: E. Schraml

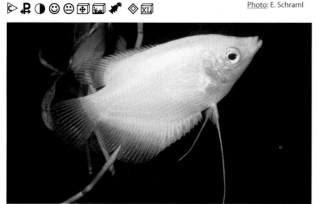

X69560-3 Osphromenus gorami "GOLD"
Golden Giant Gourami   SUBADULT
Tropical Asia, B, 60 cm

▷ ♬ ◑ ☺ 😁 ⊞ 🖼 🐾 ◈ 🔠

Photo: F. Teigler/
Archiv ACS

X69560-3 Osphromenus gorami "GOLD"
Golden Giant Gourami   SUBADULT
Tropical Asia, B, 60 cm

▷ ♬ ◑ ☺ 😁 ⊞ 🖼 🐾 ◈ 🔠

Photo: M. Smith

Pond with adult Golden Giant Gouramis

Photo: F. Schäfer

X69575-3 Osphromenus laticlavius ROBERTS, 1992
Red Giant Gourami   SUBADULT
Borneo: Sabah, W, 50 cm

▷ ♬ ◑ ☺ 😁 ⊞ 🖼 🐾 ◈ 🔠

Photo: F. Schäfer

X69575-4 Osphromenus laticlavius ROBERTS, 1992
Red Giant Gourami　　　　ADULT
Borneo: Sabah, W, 50 cm

▷ ♫ ◑ ☺ ☹ ⊞ 🖼 ⚓ ◈ ⊠

Photo: M. Smith

X69585-5 Osphromenus septemfasciatus ROBERTS, 1992
Sevenstripe Giant Gourami　　　ADULT
Borneo, W, 50 cm

▷ ♫ ◑ ☺ ☹ ⊞ 🖼 ⚓ ◈ ⊠

Photo: M. Kottelat

X75305-4 Parasphaerichthys ocellatus PARASHAD & MUKERJI, 1929
False Chocolate Gourami　　　ADULT
Burma, W, 6 cm

▷ ♫ ◑ ☺ ☹ ⊞ 🖼 ⚠ ▥

Photo: W. Foersch

X76105-5 Parosphromenus allani BROWN, 1987
Allans Licorice Gourami　　MALE　　ADULT
Borneo: Sarawak, W, 4 cm

◁ �🝙P ● ☺ ☹ ⊡ 🖼 ⚓ 🐛 ⚠ ⓢ ♂

Photo: H. Linke

X76145-5 Parosphromenus anjunganensis KOTTELAT, 1991
Anjungan Licorice Gourami　　MALE　　ADULT
Borneo: Kalimantan barat, W, 4 cm

◁ �🝙P ● ☺ ☹ ⊡ 🖼 ⚓ 🐛 ⚠ ⓢ ♂

Photo:

Parosphromenus anjunganensis KOTTELAT, 1991
Anjungan Licorice Gourami　　FEMALE　　ADULT
Borneo: Kalimantan barat, W, 4 cm

◁ �🝙P ● ☺ ☹ ⊡ 🖼 ⚓ 🐛 ⚠ ⓢ ♀

Photo: H. Linke

X76160-4 Parosphromenus deissneri (BLEEKER, 1859)
Licorice Gourami　　　MALE　　ADULT
Indonesia: Bangka, W, 4 cm

◁ ⚡P ● ☺ ☹ ⊡ 🖼 ⚓ 🐛 ⚠ ⓢ ♂

Photo: H. Linke

X76205-4 Parosphromenus cf. deissneri "BANGKA"
Licorice Gourami　　　MALE　　ADULT
Indonesia: Bangka, W, 4 cm

◁ ⚡P ● ☺ ☹ ⊡ 🖼 ⚓ 🐛 ⚠ ⓢ ♂

Photo: P. K. L. Ng

X76265-4 Parosphromenus deissneri sumatranus KLAUSEWITZ, 1955
Sumatra Licorice Gourami   MALE   ADULT
Sumatra: Jambi, W, 4 cm

◁ � P ● ☺ ☺ 🎴🖼 🐁 🐟 ⚠ Ⓢ ♂   Photo: P. K. L. Ng

X76225-4 Parosphromenus cf. deissneri
Licorice Gourami
Aquarium stock, B, 4 cm

◁ � P ● ☺ ☺ 🎴🖼 🐁 🐟 ⚠ Ⓢ ♂   Photo: J. Schmidt

X76280-4 Parosphromenus filamentosus VIERKE, 1981
Filamenttail Licorice Gourami   MALE   ADULT
Borneo, W, 4 cm

◁ � P ● ☺ ☺ 🎴🖼 🐁 🐟 ⚠ Ⓢ ♂   Photo: J. Vierke

X76280-4 Parosphromenus filamentosus VIERKE, 1981
Filamenttail Licorice Gourami   MALE   ADULT
Borneo, W, 4 cm

◁ � P ● ☺ ☺ 🎴🖼 🐁 🐟 ⚠ Ⓢ ♂   Photo: H. Linke

X76305-4 Parosphromenus harveyi BROWN, 1987
Harveys Licorice Gourami   MALE   ADULT
Malaysia: Selangor, W, 4 cm

◁ � P ● ☺ ☺ 🎴🖼 🐁 🐟 ⚠ Ⓢ ♂   Photo: H. Linke

X76305-4 Parosphromenus harveyi BROWN, 1987
Harveys Licorice Gourami   MALE   ADULT
Malaysia: Selangor, W, 4 cm

◁ � P ● ☺ ☺ 🎴🖼 🐁 🐟 ⚠ Ⓢ ♂   Photo: P. K. L. Ng

X76365-4 Parosphromenus linkei KOTTELAT, 1991
Linkes Licorice Gourami   MALE   ADULT
Borneo: Kalimantan tengah, W, 4 cm

◁ � P ● ☺ ☺ 🎴🖼 🐁 🐟 ⚠ Ⓢ ♂   Photo: G. Kopic

X76365-4 Parosphromenus linkei KOTTELAT, 1991
Linkes Licorice Gourami   MALE   ADULT
Borneo: Kalimantan tengah, W, 4 cm

◁ � P ● ☺ ☺ 🎴🖼 🐁 🐟 ⚠ Ⓢ ♂   Photo: H. Linke

X59015-4 Malpulutta kretseri "KOTTAWA FOREST"

Photo: L. Seegers

© Verlag A.C.S. GmbH

X76380-4 Parosphromenus nagyi SCHALLER, 1985
Nagys Licorice Gourami   MALE   ADULT
Malaysia: Kuantan, W, 4 cm

◁ ℙ●☺☹⬛🖼🐛🐌 ⚠️🆂♂   Photo: G. Kopic

X76380-4 Parosphromenus nagyi SCHALLER, 1985
Nagys Licorice Gourami   MALE   ADULT
Malaysia: Kuantan, W, 4 cm

◁ ℙ●☺☹⬛🖼🐛🐌 ⚠️🆂♂   Photo: H. Linke

X76445-3 Parosphromenus ornaticauda KOTTELAT, 1991
Redtail Licorice Gourami   SUBADULT
Borneo: Kalimantan barat, W, 3 cm

◁ ℙ●☺☹⬛🖼🐛🐌 ⚠️🆂   Photo: G. Kopic

X76445-4 Parosphromenus ornaticauda KOTTELAT, 1991
Redtail Licorice Gourami   MALE   ADULT
Borneo: Kalimantan barat, W, 3 cm

◁ ℙ●☺☹⬛🖼🐛🐌 ⚠️🆂♂   Photo: G. Kopic

X76445-4 Parosphromenus ornaticauda KOTTELAT, 1991
Redtail Licorice Gourami   FEMALE   ADULT
Borneo: Kalimantan barat, W, 3 cm

◁ ℙ●☺☹⬛🖼🐛🐌 ⚠️🆂♀   Photo: H. Linke

X76445-4 Parosphromenus ornaticauda KOTTELAT, 1991
Redtail Licorice Gourami   MALE   ADULT
Borneo: Kalimantan barat, W, 3 cm

◁ ℙ●☺☹⬛🖼🐛🐌 ⚠️🆂♂   Photo: P. K. L. Ng

X76460-4 Parosphromenus paludicola TWEEDIE, 1952
Swamp Licorice Gourami   MALE   ADULT
W-Malaysia, W, 4 cm

◁ ℙ●☺☹⬛🖼🐛🐌 ⚠️🆂♂   Photo: G. Kopic

X76460-4 Parosphromenus paludicola TWEEDIE, 1952
Swamp Licorice Gourami   FEMALE   ADULT
W-Malaysia, W, 4 cm

◁ ℙ●☺☹⬛🖼🐛🐌 ⚠️🆂♀   Photo: G. Kopic

X76460-4 Parosphromenus paludicola TWEEDIE, 1952
Swamp Licorice Gourami   MALE   ADULT
W-Malaysia, W, 4 cm
Photo: J. Schmidt

X76465-4 Parosphromenus paludicola "SOUTH THAILAND"
Swamp Licorice Gourami   MALE   ADULT
W-Malaysia, W, 4 cm
Photo: H. Linke

X76461-4 Parosphromenus paludicola "KUDA BRANG"
Swamp Licorice Gourami   MALE   ADULT
W-Malaysia, W, 4 cm
Photo: P. K. L. Ng

X76480-4 Parosphromenus parvulus VIERKE, 1979
Small Licorice Gourami   MALE   ADULT
S- Borneo, W, 3 cm
Photo: H. Linke

X76480-4 Parosphromenus parvulus VIERKE, 1979
Small Licorice Gourami   MALE   ADULT
S- Borneo, W, 3 cm
Photo: H. Linke

X76480-4 Parosphromenus parvulus VIERKE, 1979
Small Licorice Gourami   MALE   ADULT
S- Borneo, W, 3 cm
Photo: G. Kopic

X76504-4 Parosphromenus sp. "BINTAN"
Bintan Licorice Gourami   MALE   ADULT
Borneo: Bintan, W, 4 cm
Photo: H. Linke

X76504-4 Parosphromenus sp. "BINTAN"
Bintan Licorice Gourami   FEMALE   ADULT
Borneo: Bintan, W, 4 cm
Photo: H. Linke

© Verlag A.C.S. GmbH

X76380-5 Parosphromenus nagyi MALE

Photo: H. Linke

X76564-3 Parosphromenus sp. "PALANSAN"
Palansan Licorice Gourami   PAIR (?)
Palansan, W, 3 cm
◁ ⅃P ◑ ☺ ☺ 🔽 🖼 🦎 🐀 ⚠ Ⓢ ♂ ♀   Photo: H. Linke

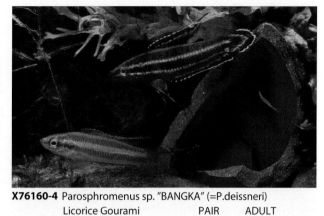

X76160-4 Parosphromenus sp. "BANGKA" (=P.deissneri)
Licorice Gourami   PAIR   ADULT
Bangka, W, 4 cm
◁ ⅃P ◑ ☺ ☺ 🔽 🖼 🦎 🐀 ⚠ Ⓢ ♂ ♀   Photo: H. Linke

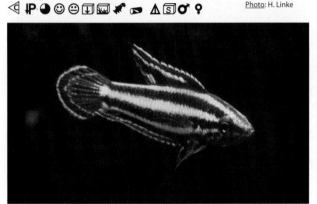

X76506-4 Parosphromenus sp. "BUKIT MERAH"
Bukit Merah Licorice Gourami   MALE   ADULT
Bukit Merah, W, 4 cm
◁ ⅃P ◑ ☺ ☺ 🔽 🖼 🦎 🐀 ⚠ Ⓢ ♂   Photo:

X76506-4 Parosphromenus sp. "BUKIT MERAH"
Bukit Merah Licorice Gourami   FEMALE   ADULT
Bukit Merah, W, 4 cm
◁ ⅃P ◑ ☺ ☺ 🔽 🖼 🦎 🐀 ⚠ Ⓢ ♀   Photo: H. Linke

X76505-4 Parosphromenus sp. "JAMBI"
Jambi Licorice Gourami   MALE   ADULT
Jambi, W, 4 cm
◁ ⅃P ◑ ☺ ☺ 🔽 🖼 🦎 🐀 ⚠ Ⓢ ♂   Photo: H. Linke

X76505-4 Parosphromenus sp. "JAMBI"
Jambi Licorice Gourami   FEMALE   ADULT
Jambi, W, 4 cm
◁ ⅃P ◑ ☺ ☺ 🔽 🖼 🦎 🐀 ⚠ Ⓢ ♀   Photo: H. Linke

X76544-2 Parosphromenus sp. "MALAKKA"
Malakka Licorice Gourami   JUVENIL
Malakka, W, 3 cm (?)
◁ ⅃P ◑ ☺ ☺ 🔽 🖼 🦎 🐀 ⚠ Ⓢ   Photo: H. Linke

X76605-4 Parosphromenus sp. "SUKAMARA"
Sukamara Licorice Gourami   MALE   ADULT
Sukamara, W, 3 cm
◁ ⅃P ◑ ☺ ☺ 🔽 🖼 🦎 🐀 ⚠ Ⓢ ♂   Photo: H. Linke

© **Verlag A.C.S. GmbH**

X82030-4 Pseudosphromenus cupanus (CUVIER & VALENCIENNES, 1831)
Red Eye Spiketail MALE ADULT
SriLanka, W, 6 cm

▷♗◗☺☺⬆🖼🦐🐌 ◈🅜 ♂ Photo: F. Teigler Archiv ACS

X82030-4 Pseudosphromenus cupanus (CUVIER & VALENCIENNES, 1831)
Red Eye Spiketail FEMALE ADULT
SriLanka, W, 6 cm

▷♗◗☺☺⬆🖼🦐🐌 ◈🅜 ♀ Photo: F. Teigler Archiv ACS

X82030-5 Pseudosphromenus cupanus (CUVIER & VALENCIENNES, 1831)
Red Eye Spiketail MALE ADULT
SriLanka, W, 6 cm

▷♗◗☺☺⬆🖼🦐🐌 ◈🅜 ♂ Photo: H. Linke

X82020-4 Pseudosphromenus cupanus (CUVIER & VALENCIENNES, 1831)
Spiketail PAIR ADULT
India, W, 6 cm

▷♗◗☺☺⬆🖼🦐🐌 ◈🅜 ♂♀ Photo: F. Schäfer

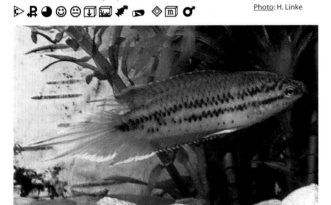

X82105-4 Pseudosphromenus dayi (ENGMANN, 1909)
Days Spiketail MALE ADULT
Malabar Coast, B, 6 cm

▷♗◗☺☺⬆🖼🦐🐌 ◈🅜 ♂ Photo: F. Teigler Archiv ACS

X82105-4 Pseudosphromenus dayi (ENGMANN, 1909)
Days Spiketail FEMALE ADULT
Malabar Coast, B, 6 cm

▷♗◗☺☺⬆🖼🦐🐌 ◈🅜 ♀ Photo: F. Teigler Archiv ACS

X82105-5 Pseudosphromenus dayi (ENGMANN, 1909)
Days Spiketail MALE ADULT
Malabar Coast, B, 6 cm

▷♗◗☺☺⬆🖼🦐🐌 ◈🅜 ♂ Photo: A. Canovas

X82105-5 Pseudosphromenus dayi (ENGMANN, 1909)
Days Spiketail FEMALE ADULT
Malabar Coast, B, 6 cm

▷♗◗☺☺⬆🖼🦐🐌 ◈🅜 ♀ Photo: A. Canovas

A80555-2 Sandelia bainsii CASTELNAU, 1861
Rockey   JUVENIL
South Africa, W, 15 cm

◁ ♫ ◑ ☺ ☻ ⊞ 🖼 ➡ ⚠ 🔟   <u>Photo</u>: D. Armitage

A80555-3 Sandelia bainsii CASTELNAU, 1861
Rockey   SUBADULT
South Africa, W, 15 cm

◁ ♫ ◑ ☺ ☻ ⊞ 🖼 ➡ ⚠ 🔟   <u>Photo</u>: W. Foersch

A80555-5 Sandelia bainsii CASTELNAU, 1861
Rockey   MALE   ADULT
South Africa, W, 15 cm

◁ ♫ ◑ ☺ ☻ ⊞ 🖼 ➡ ⚠ 🔟 ♂   <u>Photo</u>: W. Foersch

A80570-4 Sandelia capensis (CUVIER & VALENCIENNES, 1831)
Cape Kurper   MALE   ADULT
South Africa, W, 10 cm

◁ ♫ ◑ ☺ ☻ ⊞ 🖼 ➡ ⚠ 🔟 ♂   <u>Photo</u>: G. Schreiber

A80570-4 Sandelia capensis (CUVIER & VALENCIENNES, 1831)
Cape Kurper   FEMALE ADULT
South Africa, W, 10 cm

◁ ♫ ◑ ☺ ☻ ⊞ 🖼 ➡ ⚠ 🔟 ♀   <u>Photo</u>: G. Schreiber

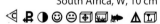

A80565-4 Sandelia capensis (= S. vicina)
Cape Kurper Var. I   ADULT
South Africa, W, 10 cm

◁ ♫ ◑ ☺ ☻ ⊞ 🖼 ➡ ⚠ 🔟   <u>Photo</u>: D. Armitage

X89400-4 Sphaerichthys acrostoma VIERKE, 1979
Large Chocolate Gourami   MALE   ADULT
Borneo, W, 10 cm

⚠ ℙ ● ☺ ☻ ⊞ 🖼 ➡ ⚠ 🔟 ♂   <u>Photo</u>: H. Linke

X89400-4 Sphaerichthys acrostoma VIERKE, 1979
Large Chocolate Gourami   PAIR   ADULT
Borneo, W, 10 cm

⚠ ℙ ● ☺ ☻ ⊞ 🖼 ➡ ⚠ 🔟 ♂ ♀   <u>Photo</u>: H. Linke

© **V e r l a g   A . C . S .   G m b H**

Photo: U. Renninger

Photo:
U. Renninger

1. Biotop von Ctenopoma damasi in Uganda
1. Biotope of Ctenopoma damasi in Uganda

2. Biotop von Ctenopoma muriei in Uganda
2. Biotope of Ctenopoma muriei in Uganda

X89420-4 Sphaerichthys o. osphromenoides (CANESTRINI, 1860)
Chocolate Gourami   MALE   ADULT
Malaysia, Indonesia, W, 6 cm
⚠ ℗ ● ☺ ☻ ⊞ 🖼 🐟 ⚠ 🔲 ♂   Photo: A. Canovas

X89420-4 Sphaerichthys o. osphromenoides (CANESTRINI, 1860)
Chocolate Gourami   FEMALE   ADULT
Malaysia, Indonesia, W, 6 cm
⚠ ℗ ● ☺ ☻ ⊞ 🖼 🐟 ⚠ 🔲 ♀   Photo: H.-J. Mayland

X89420-5 Sphaerichthys o. osphromenoides (CANESTRINI, 1860)
Chocolate Gourami   MALE   ADULT
Malaysia, Indonesia, W, 6 cm
⚠ ℗ ● ☺ ☻ ⊞ 🖼 🐟 ⚠ 🔲 ♂   Photo: H. Linke

X89420-5 Sphaerichthys o. osphromenoides (CANESTRINI, 1860)
Chocolate Gourami   FEMALE   ADULT
Malaysia, Indonesia, W, 6 cm
⚠ ℗ ● ☺ ☻ ⊞ 🖼 🐟 ⚠ 🔲 ♀   Photo: H. Linke

X89423-2 Sphaerichthys o. selatanensis VIERKE, 1979
Crossband Chocolate Gourami   JUVENIL
Borneo, W, 6 cm
⚠ ℗ ● ☺ ☻ ⊞ 🖼 🐟 ⚠ 🔲   Photo: G. Kopic

X89423-3 Sphaerichthys o. selatanensis VIERKE, 1979
Crossband Chocolate Gourami   SUBADULT
Borneo, W, 6 cm
⚠ ℗ ● ☺ ☻ ⊞ 🖼 🐟 ⚠ 🔲   Photo: G. Kopic

X89423-4 Sphaerichthys o. selatanensis VIERKE, 1979
Crossband Chocolate Gourami   MALE   ADULT
Borneo, W, 6 cm
⚠ ℗ ● ☺ ☻ ⊞ 🖼 🐟 ⚠ 🔲 ♂   Photo: H. Linke

X89455-4 Sphaerichthys vaillanti (PELLEGRIN, 1930)
Vaillants Chocolate Gourami   PAIR   ADULT
Borneo, W, 8 cm
⚠ ℗ ● ☺ ☻ ⊞ 🖼 🐟 ⚠ 🔲 ♂ ♀   Photo: O. Perrin

© Verlag A.C.S. GmbH

X89455-4 Sphaerichthys vaillanti (PELLEGRIN, 1930)
Vaillants Chocolate Gourami   MALE   mouthbrooding!
Borneo, W, 8 cm

⚠ ℙ ◑ ☺ ☹ ⊞ 🔲 ➤ ⚠ m ♂
Photo: O. Perrin

X89455-4 Sphaerichthys vaillanti (PELLEGRIN, 1930)
Vaillants Chocolate Gourami   FEMALE   ADULT
Borneo, W, 8 cm

⚠ ℙ ◑ ☺ ☹ ⊞ 🔲 ➤ ⚠ m ♀
Photo: O. Perrin

X93005-2 Trichogaster leerii (BLEEKER, 1861)
Pearl Gourami   JUVENIL
Malaysia, Indonesia, B, 12 cm

▷ ฿ ◑ ☺ ☹ ⊞ 🔲 🔑 ◈ m
Photo: F. Teigler
Archiv ACS

X93005-3 Trichogaster leerii (BLEEKER, 1861)
Pearl Gourami   MALE   SUBADULT
Malaysia, Indonesia, B, 12 cm

▷ ฿ ◑ ☺ ☹ ⊞ 🔲 🔑 ◈ m ♂
Photo: F. Teigler
Archiv ACS

X93005-5 Trichogaster leerii (BLEEKER, 1861)
Pearl Gourami   MALE   ADULT
Malaysia, Indonesia, B, 12 cm

▷ ฿ ◑ ☺ ☹ ⊞ 🔲 🔑 ◈ m ♂
Photo: J. Glaser

X93005-5 Trichogaster leerii (BLEEKER, 1861)
Pearl Gourami   FEMALE   ADULT
Malaysia, Indonesia, B, 12 cm

▷ ฿ ◑ ☺ ☹ ⊞ 🔲 🔑 ◈ m ♀
Photo: U. Werner

X93006-4 Trichogaster leerii (BLEEKER, 1861)
Pearl Gourami "WILD"   PAIR   ADULT
Malaysia, W, 12 cm

▷ ฿ ◑ ☺ ☹ ⊞ 🔲 🔑 ◈ m ♂ ♀
Photo: F. Teigler
Archiv ACS

X93015-4 Trichogaster leerii "GOLD"
Golden Pearl Gourami   FEMALE   ADULT
Breeding form, B, 12 cm

▷ ฿ ◑ ☺ ☹ ⊞ 🔲 🔑 ◈ m ♀
Photo: J. Dawes

X93045-2 Trichogaster microlepis (GÜNTHER, 1861)
Moonlight Gourami   JUVENIL
Thailand, Malaysia, B, 20 cm

Photo: F. Teigler
Archiv ACS

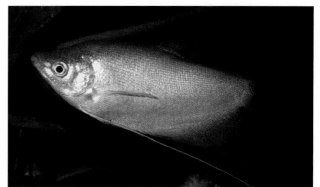

X93045-5 Trichogaster microlepis (GÜNTHER, 1861)
Moonlight Gourami   MALE   ADULT
Thailand, Malaysia, B, 20 cm

Photo: E. Schraml

X93045-4 Trichogaster microlepis (GÜNTHER, 1861)
Moonlight Gourami   MALE   ADULT
Thailand, Malaysia, B, 20 cm

Photo: Archiv ACS
Migge/Reinhard

X93045-4 Trichogaster microlepis (GÜNTHER, 1861)
Moonlight Gourami   FEMALE   ADULT
Thailand, Malaysia, B, 20 cm

Photo: Archiv ACS
Migge/Reinhard

X93065-2 Trichogaster pectoralis (REGAN, 1909)
Snakeskin Gourami   JUVENIL
Thailand, B, 20 cm

Photo: J. Vierke

X93065-3 Trichogaster pectoralis (REGAN, 1909)
Snakeskin Gourami   SUBADULT
Thailand, B, 20 cm

Photo: B. Teichfischer

X93065-4 Trichogaster pectoralis (REGAN, 1909)
Snakeskin Gourami   MALE   ADULT
Thailand, B, 20 cm

Photo: A. Canovas

X93065-5 Trichogaster pectoralis (REGAN, 1909)
Snakeskin Gourami   MALE   ADULT
Thailand, B, 20 cm

Photo: J. Vierke

© Verlag A.C.S. GmbH

X93205-4 Trichogaster t. trichopterus (PALLAS, 1777)
Spotted Gourami   MALE   ADULT
Thailand, Malaysia, Indonesia, W, 15 cm

▷♨◑☺☹⊞🐌🦐 ◈🔲 ♂   Photo: F. Teigler Archiv ACS

X93205-4 Trichogaster t. trichopterus (PALLAS, 1777)
Spotted Gourami   FEMALE   ADULT
Thailand, Malaysia, Indonesia, W, 15 cm

▷♨◑☺☹⊞🐌🦐 ◈🔲 ♀   Photo: F. Teigler Archiv ACS

X93225-4 Trichogaster t. trichopterus (PALLAS, 1777)
Spotted Gourami Var.1   MALE   ADULT
C-Thailand: Ayuthayia, W, 15 cm

▷♨◑☺☹⊞🐌🦐 ◈🔲 ♂   Photo: H.-J. Günther

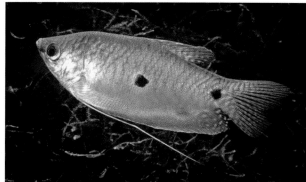

X93245-4 Trichogaster t. trichopterus (PALLAS, 1777)
Spotted Gourami Var.2   FEMALE   ADULT
Sumatra: Sibolga, W, 15 cm

▷♨◑☺☹⊞🐌🦐 ◈🔲 ♀   Photo: H. Linke

X93265-5 Trichogaster t. trichopterus (PALLAS, 1777)
Spotted Gourami Var.3   ADULT
S-Thailand, W, 15 cm

▷♨◑☺☹⊞🐌🦐 ◈🔲   Photo: J. Vierke

X93285-4 Trichogaster t. trichopterus (PALLAS, 1777)
Spotted Gourami Var.4   PAIR   ADULT
Borneo, W, 15 cm

▷♨◑☺☹⊞🐌🦐 ◈🔲 ♂ ♀   Photo: J. Schmidt

X93185-5 Trichogaster t. sumatranus LADIGES, 1933
Blue Gourami   MALE   ADULT
Sumatra, B, 15 cm

▷♨◑☺☹⊞🐌🦐 ◈🔲 ♂   Photo: Archiv ACS Migge/Reinhard

X93185-5 Trichogaster t. sumatranus LADIGES, 1933
Blue Gourami   FEMALE   ADULT
Sumatra, B, 15 cm

▷♨◑☺☹⊞🐌🦐 ◈🔲 ♀   Photo: Archiv ACS Migge/Reinhard

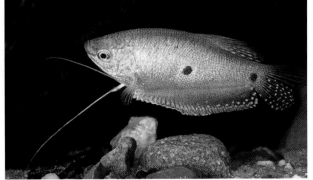

X93166-4 Trichogaster trichopterus "STEELBLUE"
Steelblue Gourami MALE ADULT
Breeding Form, B, 15 cm

Photo: F. Teigler Archiv ACS

X93166-4 Trichogaster trichopterus "STEELBLUE"
Steelblue Gourami FEMALE ADULT
Breeding Form, B, 15 cm

Photo: F. Teigler Archiv ACS

X93126-4 Trichogaster trichopterus "LIGHT BLUE"
Light Blue Gourami MALE ADULT
Breeding Form, B, 15 cm

Photo: F. Teigler Archiv ACS

X93126-4 Trichogaster trichopterus "LIGHT BLUE"
Light Blue Gourami FEMALE ADULT
Breeding Form, B, 15 cm

Photo: F. Teigler Archiv ACS

X93325-4 Trichogaster trichopterus "GOLD"
Gold Gourami MALE ADULT
Breeding Form, B, 15 cm

Photo: F. Teigler Archiv ACS

X93325-4 Trichogaster trichopterus "GOLD"
Gold Gourami FEMALE ADULT
Breeding Form, B, 15 cm

Photo: F. Teigler Archiv ACS

X93305-3 Trichogaster trichopterus "COSBY"
Cosby Gourami SUBADULT
Breeding Form, B, 15 cm

Photo: J. Glaser

X93305-5 Trichogaster trichopterus "COSBY"
Cosby Gourami MALE ADULT
Breeding Form, B, 15 cm

Photo: A. Canovas

© Verlag A.C.S. GmbH

X94166-5 Trichopsis vittata "DOUBLE SPOT"   MALE

Photo: H.-J. Mayland

X93305-5 Trichogaster trichopterus "COSBY"
Cosby Gourami FEMALE ADULT
Breeding Form, B, 15 cm

Photo: Archiv ACS
Migge/Reinhard

X93165-4 Trichogaster trichopterus "OPAL"
Opal Gourami PAIR ADULT
Breeding Form, B, 15 cm

Photo: F. Teigler
Archiv ACS

X94025-4 Trichopsis pumila (ARNOLD, 1936)
Pygmy Gourami MALE ADULT
Thailand, Malaysia, Indonesia, W, 4 cm

Photo: H.-G. Evers

X94025-4 Trichopsis pumila (ARNOLD, 1936)
Pygmy Gourami FEMALE ADULT
Thailand, Malaysia, Indonesia, W, 4 cm

Photo: M. Smith

X94025-5 Trichopsis pumila (ARNOLD, 1936)
Pygmy Gourami MALE ADULT
Thailand, Malaysia, Indonesia, W, 4 cm

Photo: B. Teichfischer

X94126-4 Trichopsis cf. schalleri "KAENG KRACHAN DAM"
Kaeng Krachan Dam Gourami
Malaysia, W, 6 cm

Photo: J. Schmidt

X94085-4 Trichopsis schalleri LADIGES, 1962
Schallers Gourami MALE ADULT
S-Thailand, W, 6 cm

Photo: H. Linke

X94085-4 Trichopsis schalleri LADIGES, 1962
Schallers Gourami FEMALE ADULT
S-Thailand, W, 6 cm

Photo: H. Linke

© Verlag A.C.S. GmbH

X94085-4 Trichopsis schalleri LADIGES, 1962
Schallers Gourami   MALE   ADULT
S-Thailand, W, 6 cm

▷♬◑☺☻⊞🖼🦎🐌 ◈⑤♂   Photo: J. Schmidt

X94005-4 Trichopsis vittata x schalleri
Hybrid Croaking Gourami   MALE   ADULT
Breeding Form, X, 6 cm

▷♬◑☺☻⊞🖼🦎🐌 ◈⑤♂   Photo: J. Vierke

X94225-4 Trichopsis vittata (CUVIER & VALENCIENNES, 1831)
Croaking Gourami   MALE   ADULT
Aquarium Stock, B, 6 cm

▷♬◑☺☻⊞🖼🦎🐌 ◈⑤♂   Photo: B. Teichfischer

X94225-4 Trichopsis vittata (CUVIER & VALENCIENNES, 1831)
Croaking Gourami   FEMALE   ADULT
Aquarium Stock, B, 6 cm

▷♬◑☺☻⊞🖼🦎🐌 ◈⑤♀   Photo: B. Teichfischer

X94226-3 Trichopsis vittata (CUVIER & VALENCIENNES, 1831)
Croaking Gourami   MALE   SUBADULT
Malaysia, W, 6 cm

▷♬◑☺☻⊞🖼🦎🐌 ◈⑤♂   Photo: F. Teigler
                                   Archiv ACS

X94226-3 Trichopsis vittata (CUVIER & VALENCIENNES, 1831)
Croaking Gourami   FEMALE   SUBADULT
Malaysia, W, 6 cm

▷♬◑☺☻⊞🖼🦎🐌 ◈⑤♀   Photo: F. Teigler
                                   Archiv ACS

X94226-5 Trichopsis vittata (CUVIER & VALENCIENNES, 1831)
Croaking Gourami   MALE   ADULT
Malaysia, W, 6 cm

▷♬◑☺☻⊞🖼🦎🐌 ◈⑤♂   Photo: F. Teigler
                                   Archiv ACS

X94226-5 Trichopsis vittata (CUVIER & VALENCIENNES, 1831)
Croaking Gourami   FEMALE   ADULT
Malaysia, W, 6 cm

▷♬◑☺☻⊞🖼🦎🐌 ◈⑤♀   Photo: F. Teigler
                                   Archiv ACS

X94227-4 Trichopsis vittata "KAENG KRACHAN DAM"
Croaking Gourami   MALE   ADULT
Malaysia, W, 6 cm

▷ ♬ ◑ ☺ ☺ ⊞ 🖼 🦎 🐌 ◈ Ⓢ ♂   Photo: J. Schmidt

X94228-4 Trichopsis vittata "TRENGGAM KUANTAN"
Croaking Gourami   MALE   ADULT
Malaysia, W, 6 cm

▷ ♬ ◑ ☺ ☺ ⊞ 🖼 🦎 🐌 ◈ Ⓢ ♂   Photo: P. K. L. Ng

X94166-4 Trichopsis vittata "DOUBLE SPOT"
Croaking Gourami   MALE   ADULT
Thailand, W, 6 cm

▷ ♬ ◑ ☺ ☺ ⊞ 🖼 🦎 🐌 ◈ Ⓢ ♂   Photo: H. Linke

X94166-4 Trichopsis vittata "DOUBLE SPOT"
Croaking Gourami   FEMALE   ADULT
Thailand, W, 6 cm

▷ ♬ ◑ ☺ ☺ ⊞ 🖼 🦎 🐌 ◈ Ⓢ ♀   Photo: H. Linke

X94165-4 Trichopsis vittata "BLUE" (= T. harrisi)
Blue Croaking Gourami   MALE   ADULT
Thailand, Borneo, W, 6 cm

▷ ♬ ◑ ☺ ☺ ⊞ 🖼 🦎 🐌 ◈ Ⓢ ♂   Photo: G. Kopic

X94165-4 Trichopsis vittata "BLUE" (= T. harrisi)
Blue Croaking Gourami   FEMALE   ADULT
Thailand, Borneo, W, 6 cm

▷ ♬ ◑ ☺ ☺ ⊞ 🖼 🦎 🐌 ◈ Ⓢ ♀   Photo: G. Kopic

X08505-4 Badis badis badis (HAMILTON-BUCHANAN, 1822)
Blue Dwarf   PAIR   ADULT
India, W, 6 cm

▷ ♬ ◑ ☺ ⊞ 🖼 🐌 ◈ Ⓢ ♂ ♀   Photo: F. Teigler
                                              Archiv ACS

X08506-5 Badis badis badis (HAMILTON-BUCHANAN, 1822)
Blue Dwarf   MALE   ADULT
Aquarium stock, B, 6 cm

▷ ♬ ◑ ☺ ⊞ 🖼 🐌 ◈ Ⓢ ♂   Photo: H.-J. Mayland

X08655-4 Badis badis burmanicus AHL, 1936
  Burma Chameleon Fish MALE ADULT
  Burma, B, 6 cm

▷♬◑☺⬜🖼🐟◈⑤♂   Photo:F. Schäfer

X08655-4 Badis badis burmanicus AHL, 1936
  Burma Chameleon Fish FEMALE ADULT
  Burma, B, 6 cm

▷♬◑☺⬜🖼🐟◈⑤♀   Photo: F. Schäfer

X08705-4 Badis badis siamensis KLAUSEWITZ, 1957
  Siamese Chameleon Fish MALE ADULT
  Thailand: Phuket, W, 6 cm

▷♬◑☺⬜🖼🐟◈⑤♂   Photo: J. Schmidt

X08705-4 Badis badis siamensis KLAUSEWITZ, 1957
  Siamese Chameleon Fish FEMALE ADULT
  Thailand: Phuket, W, 6 cm

▷♬◑☺⬜🖼🐟◈⑤♀   Photo: J. Schmidt

X85507-4 Badis badis "ASSAM" (B. b. assamensis AHL, 1936?)
  Assam Chameleon Fish MALE ADULT
  Assam, W, 6 cm

▷♬◑☺⬜🖼🐟◈⑤♂   Photo: L. Seegers

X80005-2 Pristolepis fasciata (BLEEKER, 1851)
  Tiger Nandid   JUVENIL
  Thailand, W, 15 cm

▷♬◑☺⬜🖼🐟◈Ⓛ   Photo: H.-J. Günther

X80005-4 Pristolepis fasciata (BLEEKER, 1851)
  Tiger Nandid   ADULT
  Thailand, W, 15 cm

▷♬◑☺⬜🖼🐟◈Ⓛ   Photo: H.-J. Günther

X80005-4 Pristolepis fasciata (BLEEKER, 1851)
  Tiger Nandid   ADULT
  Thailand, W, 15 cm

▷♬◑☺⬜🖼🐟◈Ⓛ   Photo: H.-J. Günther

X80005-5 Pristolepis fasciata (BLEEKER, 1851) preserved specimen
Tiger Nandid   ADULT
Thailand, W, 15 cm
▷ ⊮ ◑ ☺ 🎲 🖼 ➡ ◈ 🔲   Photo: M. Kottelat

X80055-2 Pristolepis grooti (BLEEKER, 1851)
Malayian Tiger Nandid   JUVENIL
Malaysia, Indonesia, W, 15 cm
▷ ⊮ ◑ ☺ 🎲 🖼 ➡ ◈ 🔲   Photo: P. K. L. Ng

X80055-5 Pristolepis grooti (BLEEKER, 1851)
Malayian Tiger Nandid   ADULT
Malaysia, Indonesia, W, 15 cm
▷ ⊮ ◑ ☺ 🎲 🖼 ➡ ◈ 🔲   Photo: M. Kottelat

A00140-4 Afronandus sheljuzkhoi (MEINKEN, 1954)
African Nandid   ADULT
Ivory Coast, W, 10 cm
▷ ⅃Ρ ◑ ☺ 🎲 🖼 ➡ ⚠ 🔲   Photo: L. Seegers

A00140-4 Afronandus sheljuzkhoi (MEINKEN, 1954)
African Nandid   ADULT
Ivory Coast, W, 10 cm
▷ ⅃Ρ ◑ ☺ 🎲 🖼 ➡ ⚠ 🔲   Photo: L. Seegers

A00140-4 Afronandus sheljuzkhoi (MEINKEN, 1954)
African Nandid   ADULT
Ivory Coast, W, 10 cm
▷ ⅃Ρ ◑ ☺ 🎲 🖼 ➡ ⚠ 🔲   Photo: L. Seegers

A00140-4 Afronandus sheljuzkhoi (MEINKEN, 1954)
African Nandid   ADULT
Ivory Coast, W, 10 cm
▷ ⅃Ρ ◑ ☺ 🎲 🖼 ➡ ⚠ 🔲   Photo: L. Seegers

X66110-5 Nandus nandus (HAMILTON, 1822) preserved specimen
Common Nandid   ADULT
India, W, 15 cm
▷ ⊮ ◑ ☺ 🎲 🖼 ➡ ◈ 🔲   Photo: C. C. Vidhayanon

X66110-4 Nandus nandus (HAMILTON, 1822) preserved specimen
Common Nandid   ADULT
India, W, 15 cm

▷ ♣ ◑ ☺ ☷ ▦ ➤ ◈ ▦   Photo: M. Kottelat

X66110-2 Nandus nandus (HAMILTON, 1822)
Common Nandid   JUVENIL
India, W, 15 cm

▷ ♣ ◑ ☺ ☷ ▦ ➤ ◈ ▦   Photo: A. Canovas

X66110-2 Nandus nandus (HAMILTON, 1822)
Common Nandid   JUVENIL
India, W, 15 cm

▷ ♣ ◑ ☺ ☷ ▦ ➤ ◈ ▦   Photo: A. Canovas

X66155-4 Nandus nebulosus (GRAY, 1830) preserved specimen
Small Nandid   ADULT
Malaysia, Indonesia, W, 10 cm

▷ ♣ ◑ ☺ ☷ ▦ ➤ ◈ ▦   Photo: M. Kottelat

X66155-4 Nandus nebulosus (GRAY, 1830)
Small Nandid   ADULT
Malaysia, Indonesia, W, 10 cm

▷ ♣ ◑ ☺ ☷ ▦ ➤ ◈ ▦   Photo: F. Schäfer

X66165-5 Nandus oxyrhynchus NG, VIDTHAYANON & NG, 1996
Highbody Nandid   ADULT (preserved specimen)
Thailand, W, 15 cm (?)

▷ ♣ ◑ ☺ ☷ ▦ ➤ ◈ ▦   Photo: C.C. Vidthayanon

X66165-4 Nandus oxyrhynchus NG, VIDTHAYANON & NG, 1996
Highbody Nandid   ADULT (preserved specimen)
Thailand, W, 15 cm (?)

▷ ♣ ◑ ☺ ☷ ▦ ➤ ◈ ▦   Photo: M. Kottelat

X66165-4 Nandus oxyrhynchus NG, VIDTHAYANON & NG, 1996
Highbody Nandid   ADULT
Thailand, W, 15 cm (?)

▷ ♣ ◑ ☺ ☷ ▦ ➤ ◈ ▦   Photo: H.-J. Günther

X94025-5 Trichopsis pumila   MALE

Photo: J. Schmidt

© Verlag A.C.S. GmbH

X08655-5 Badis badis burmanicus   MALE   ADULT

Photo: H.-J. Mayland

X08655-3 Badis badis burmanicus   MALE   SUBADULT

Photo: H.-J. Mayland

S52705-4 Monocirrhus polyacanthus HECKEL, 1840
Leaffish ADULT
Tropical South America: Amazon Area, W, 12 cm

▷ IP ◑ ⊗ ⊡ ▦ ⇢ ⚠ ▣ Photo: Archiv ACS
Migge(Reinhard

S52705-5 Monocirrhus polyacanthus HECKEL, 1840
Leaffish ADULT
Tropical South America: Amazon Area, W, 12 cm

▷ IP ◑ ⊗ ⊡ ▦ ⇢ ⚠ ▣ Photo: H.-J. Mayland

S52705-4 Monocirrhus polyacanthus HECKEL, 1840
Leaffish ADULT
Tropical South America: Amazon Area, W, 12 cm

▷ IP ◑ ⊗ ⊡ ▦ ⇢ ⚠ ▣ Photo: F. Schäfer

S65705-3 Polycentrus schomburgki MÜLLER & TROSCHEL, 1840
Schomburgks Leaffish SUBADULT
South America: Guayanas, Trinidad, W, 8 cm

▷ IP ◑ ☺ ⊡ ▦ ⇢ ⚠ ▣ Photo: Archiv ACS
Migge(Reinhard

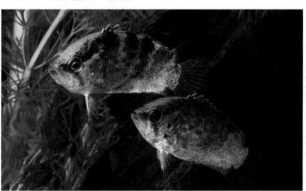

S65705-4 Polycentrus schomburgki MÜLLER & TROSCHEL, 1840
Schomburgks Leaffish PAIR ADULT
South America: Guayanas, Trinidad, W, 8 cm

▷ IP ◑ ☺ ⊡ ▦ ⇢ ⚠ ▣ ♂ ♀ Photo: F. Teigler
Archiv ACS

S65706-5 Polycentrus schomburgki MÜLLER & TROSCHEL, 1840
Schomburgks Leaffish MALE ADULT
Trinidad, W, 8 cm

▷ IP ◑ ☺ ⊡ ▦ ⇢ ⚠ ▣ ♂ Photo: J. Schmidt

S65706-4 Polycentrus schomburgki MÜLLER & TROSCHEL, 1840
Schomburgks Leaffish FEMALE ADULT
Trinidad, W, 8 cm

▷ IP ◑ ☺ ⊡ ▦ ⇢ ⚠ ▣ ♀ Photo: J. Schmidt

A70000-4 Polycentropsis abbreviata BOULENGER, 1901
African Leaffish ADULT
West Africa, W, 8 cm

▷ IP ◑ ☺ ⊡ ▦ ⇢ ⚠ ▣ Photo: Archiv ACS
Migge(Reinhard

© Verlag A.C.S. GmbH

A19780-3 Channa africana (STEINDACHNER, 1879)
African Snakehead   SUBADULT
West Africa, W, 40 cm

Photo: E. Schraml
Archiv ACS

A19780-3 Channa africana (STEINDACHNER, 1879)
African Snakehead   SUBADULT
West Africa, W, 40 cm

Photo: E. Schraml
Archiv ACS

A19780-4 Channa africana (STEINDACHNER, 1879)
African Snakehead   ADULT
West Africa, W, 40 cm

Photo: F. Teigler
Archiv ACS

A19781-3 Channa africana (STEINDACHNER, 1879)
African Snakehead Var.I   SUBADULT
West Africa, W, 40 cm

Photo: M. Smith

X37015-4 Channa argus warpachowskii BERG, 1909
Eastern Snakehead   ADULT
Russia: Chabarowsk, W, 80 cm

Photo: S. Inselmann

X37055-3 Channa asiatica (LINNE, 1758)
Chinese Snakehead   SUBADULT
SO-China, W, 35 cm

Photo: H.-J. Günther

X37055-3 Channa asiatica (LINNE, 1758)
Chinese Snakehead   SUBADULT
SO-China, W, 35 cm

Photo: M. Smith

X37075-3 Channa bankanensis (BLEEKER, 1852)
Bangka Snakehead   SUBADULT
SO-Asia: E-Malaysia, Kuching, W, 25 cm

Photo: P. K. L. Ng

X37075-3 Channa bankanensis (BLEEKER, 1852)preserved specimen
Bangka Snakehead　　　　　　　　SUBADULT
SO-Asia, W, 25 cm

Photo: M. Kottelat

X37085-4 Channa baramensis (STEINDACHNER, 1901)
Barama Snakehead　　　　　　　　ADULT
Borneo: Sabah, Beaufort area, W, 25 cm

Photo: P. K. L. Ng

X37205-2 Channa bleheri VIERKE, 1991
Rainbow Snakehead　　　　　　　　JUVENIL
Burma, W, 20 cm

Photo: J. Vierke

X37205-5 Channa bleheri VIERKE, 1991
Rainbow Snakehead　　　　　　　　ADULT
Burma, W, 20 cm

Photo: H. H. Tan

X37205-4 Channa bleheri VIERKE, 1991
Rainbow Snakehead　　　　　　　　ADULT
Burma, W, 20 cm

Photo: E. Schraml
Archiv ACS

X37315-2 Channa gachua (HAMILTON-BUCHANAN, 1822)
Frog Snakehead　　　　　　　　JUVENIL
India, W, 15 cm

Photo: F. Teigler
Archiv ACS

X37315-3 Channa gachua (HAMILTON-BUCHANAN, 1822)
Frog Snakehead　　　　　　　　SUBADULT
India, W, 15 cm

Photo: F. Teigler
Archiv ACS

X37315-4 Channa gachua (HAMILTON-BUCHANAN, 1822)
Frog Snakehead　　　　　　　　ADULT
India, W, 15 cm

Photo: J. Schmidt

X37316-4 Channa gachua (HAMILTON-BUCHANAN, 1822)
Frog Snakehead Var. I   ADULT
Sri Lanka, W, 15 cm
▷ ♫ ◐ ☺ ☹ ⬇ 🖼 ➤ ⚠ 🎦   Photo: H.-J. Günther

X37317-4 Channa gachua (HAMILTON-BUCHANAN, 1822)
Frog Snakehead Var. II   ADULT
Thailand, W, 15 cm
▷ ♫ ◐ ☺ ☹ ⬇ 🖼 ➤ ⚠ 🎦   Photo: H.-J. Günther

A19782-4 Channa insignis (SAUVAGE, 1884)
Light African Snakehead   SUBADULT
C-Africa, W, 35 cm
▷ ♫ ◐ ☺ ☹ ⬇ 🖼 ➤ ⚠ 🎦   Photo: M. Smith

A19782-5 Channa insignis (SAUVAGE, 1884)
Light African Snakehead   ADULT
C-Africa, W, 35 cm
▷ ♫ ◐ ☺ ☹ ⬇ 🖼 ➤ ⚠ 🎦   Photo: J. Schmidt

X37455-1 Channa lucia (CUVIER & VALENCIENNES, 1831)
Splendid Snakehead   BABY
SE-Asia, W, 40 cm
▷ ♫ ◐ ☺ ☹ ⬇ 🖼 ➤ ⚠ 🎦   Photo: H.-J. Günther

X37455-2 Channa lucia (CUVIER & VALENCIENNES, 1831)
Splendid Snakehead   JUVENIL
SE-Asia, W, 40 cm
▷ ♫ ◐ ☺ ☹ ⬇ 🖼 ➤ ⚠ 🎦   Photo: J. Geck

X37455-2 Channa lucia (CUVIER & VALENCIENNES, 1831)
Splendid Snakehead   JUVENIL
SE-Asia, W, 40 cm
▷ ♫ ◐ ☺ ☹ ⬇ 🖼 ➤ ⚠ 🎦   Photo: J. Vierke

X37455-3 Channa lucia (CUVIER & VALENCIENNES, 1831)
Splendid Snakehead   SUBADULT
SE-Asia, W, 40 cm
▷ ♫ ◐ ☺ ☹ ⬇ 🖼 ➤ ⚠ 🎦   Photo: E. Schraml

X37455-3 Channa lucia (CUVIER & VALENCIENNES, 1831)
Splendid Snakehead SUBADULT
SE-Asia, W, 40 cm
Photo: E. Schraml

X37455-4 Channa lucia (CUVIER & VALENCIENNES, 1831)
Splendid Snakehead ADULT
SE-Asia, W, 40 cm
Photo: H.-J. Günther

X37455-5 Channa lucia (CUVIER & VALENCIENNES, 1831)
Splendid Snakehead ADULT
SE-Asia, W, 40 cm
Photo: J. Geck

X37455-4 Channa lucia (CUVIER & VALENCIENNES, 1831)
Splendid Snakehead ADULT
SE-Asia, W, 40 cm
Photo: M. Kottelat

X37555-1 Channa marulia (HAMILTON-BUCHANAN, 1822)
Indian Snakehead BABY
S-Asia, W, 120 cm
Photo: M. Smith

X37555-2 Channa marulia (HAMILTON-BUCHANAN, 1822)
Indian Snakehead JUVENIL
S-Asia, W, 120 cm
Photo: H.-J. Mayland

X37555-3 Channa marulia (HAMILTON-BUCHANAN, 1822)
Indian Snakehead SUBADULT
S-Asia, W, 120 cm
Photo: E. Schraml
Archiv ACS

X37555-4 Channa marulia (HAMILTON-BUCHANAN, 1822)
Indian Snakehead ADULT
S-Asia, W, 120 cm
Photo: J. Schmidt

© Verlag A.C.S. GmbH

X37605-2 Channa marulioides (BLEEKER, 1851)
Darkfin Snakehead   JUVENIL
Malaysia, Indonesia, W, 65 cm
▷⚑◑☺⊗⬇⬛� ⚠☒   Photo: P. K. L. Ng

X37605-4 Channa marulioides (BLEEKER, 1851)
Darkfin Snakehead   ADULT
Malaysia, Indonesia, W, 65 cm
▷⚑◑☺⊗⬇⬛➤ ⚠☒   Photo: J. Geck

X37605-4 Channa marulioides (BLEEKER, 1851)
Darkfin Snakehead   SUBADULT
Malaysia, Indonesia, W, 65 cm
▷⚑◑☺⊗⬇⬛➤ ⚠☒   Photo: M. Kottelat

X37755-1 Channa micropeltes (CUVIER & VALENCIENNES, 1831)
Giant Snakehead   BABY
Tropical Asia, W, 100 cm
▷⚑◑☺⊗⬇⬛➤ ⚠☒   Photo: M. Smith

X37755-4 Channa micropeltes (CUVIER & VALENCIENNES, 1831)
Giant Snakehead   ADULT
Tropical Asia, W, 100 cm
▷⚑◐☺⊗⬇⬛➤ ⚠☒   Photo: H.-J. Mayland

X37755-5 Channa micropeltes (CUVIER & VALENCIENNES, 1831)
Giant Snakehead   ADULT
Tropical Asia, W, 100 cm
▷⚑◑☺⊗⬇⬛➤ ⚠☒   Photo: E. Schraml

A19788-1 Channa obscura (GÜNTHER, 1861)
Dark African Snakehead   BABY
W-Africa, W, 35 cm
▷⚑◐☺⊗⬇⬛➤ ⚠☒   Photo: F. Teigler
Archiv ACS

A19788-2 Channa obscura (GÜNTHER, 1861)
Dark African Snakehead   JUVENIL
W-Africa, W, 35 cm
▷⚑◐☺⊗⬇⬛➤ ⚠☒   Photo: J. Pinhard
Archiv ACS

X08506-5 Badis badis badis   MALE

Photo: H.-J. Mayland

© Verlag A.C.S. GmbH

X37205-5 Channa bleheri

Photo: H.-J. Mayland

A19788-3 Channa obscura (GÜNTHER, 1861)
Dark African Snakehead SUBADULT
W-Africa, W, 35 cm
Photo: E. Pürzl

A19788-4 Channa obscura (GÜNTHER, 1861)
Dark African Snakehead ADULT
W-Africa, W, 35 cm
Photo: J. Pinhard
Archiv ACS

A19788-5 Channa obscura (GÜNTHER, 1861)
Dark African Snakehead ADULT
W-Africa, W, 35 cm
Photo: Archiv ACS
Migge/Reinhard

X37385-4 Channa orientalis BLOCH & SCHNEIDER, 1801
Ceylon Snakehead ADULT
Sri Lanka, W, 15 cm
Photo: J. Vierke

X37385-4 Channa orientalis BLOCH & SCHNEIDER, 1801
Ceylon Snakehead ADULT
Sri Lanka, W, 15 cm
Photo: H.-J. Günther

X37385-4 Channa orientalis BLOCH & SCHNEIDER, 1801
Ceylon Snakehead ADULT
Sri Lanka, W, 15 cm
Photo: G. Kopic

X37385-4 Channa orientalis BLOCH & SCHNEIDER, 1801
Ceylon Snakehead ADULT
Sri Lanka, W, 15 cm
Photo: J. Schmidt

X37395-4 Channa pleurophthalma (BLEEKER, 1850)
Eyespot Snakehead ADULT
Sumatra, Borneo, W, 40 cm
Photo: H. H. Tan

X37395-4 Channa pleurophthalma (BLEEKER, 1850)
Eyespot Snakehead   ADULT
Sumatra, Borneo, W, 40 cm

Photo: M. Kottelat

X37925-4 Channa punctata (BLOCH, 1793)
Spotted Snakehead   ADULT
India, W, 35 cm

Photo: J. Vierke

X37970-2 Channa sp. "BURMA I"
Lake Inle Snakehead   JUVENIL
Burma: Lake Inle, W, 20 cm (?)

Photo: T. Luckenbach

X37970-4 Channa sp. "BURMA I"
Lake Inle Snakehead   ADULT (?)
Burma: Lake Inle, W, 20 cm (?)

Photo: T. Luckenbach

X37971-4 Channa sp. "BURMA II"
Irawaddy River Snakehead   ADULT (?)
Burma: Irawaddy River basin, W, 25 cm (?)

Photo: T. Luckenbach

X37972-2 Channa stewartii (PLAYFAIR, 1867)
Golden Snakehead   JUVENIL
NE-India, W, 25 cm

Photo: E. Schraml
Archiv ACS

X37972-3 Channa stewartii (PLAYFAIR, 1867)
Golden Snakehead   SUBADULT
NE-India, W, 25 cm

Photo: M. Smith

X37972-4 Channa stewartii (PLAYFAIR, 1867)
Golden Snakehead   ADULT
NE-India, W, 25 cm

Photo: H.-J. Mayland

X37972-5 Channa stewartii (PLAYFAIR, 1867)
Golden Snakehead ADULT
NE-India, W, 25 cm

Photo: J. Vierke

X37973-1 Channa striata (BLOCH, 1793)
Striped Snakehead BABY
Tropical Asia, W, 100 cm

Photo: H.-J. Günther

X37973-2 Channa striata (BLOCH, 1793)
Striped Snakehead JUVENIL
Tropical Asia, W, 100 cm

Photo: H.-J. Günther

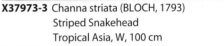

X37973-3 Channa striata (BLOCH, 1793)
Striped Snakehead SUBADULT
Tropical Asia, W, 100 cm

Photo: J. Schmidt

X37973-4 Channa striata (BLOCH, 1793)
Striped Snakehead ADULT
Tropical Asia, W, 100 cm

Photo: J. Geck

Dieser und alle anderen in
This and all other in
"all Killis of the Old World I"

Photo: F. Teigler
Archiv ACS

Dieser und alle anderen in
This and all other in
"all Killis of the Old World II"

Photo: D. Bork
Archiv ACS

Dieser und alle anderen in
This and all other in
"all Killis of the New World "

Photo: L. Seegers

© **Verlag A.C.S. GmbH**

X13115-4 Belontia signata jonklaasi   Männchen mit Eiern/*Male with eggs*   Photo: J. Vierke

X18510-4 Betta splendens Männchen unter dem Schaumnest/*Male under the bubblenest* Photo: H. Linke

X18510-4 Betta splendens Laichendes Paar/*Spawning pair* Photo: H. Linke

  © Verlag A.C.S. GmbH

X17915-4 Betta smaragdina sind Höhlenbrüter unter den schaumnestbauenden Kampffischen

Betta smaragdina are cavebrooders among the bubblenestbuilding Fighters

Photo: H. Linke

X40245-4 Colisa lalia "RAINBOW": das Männchen setzt zur Umschlingung des Weibchens an. Colisa lalia verarbeitet viel pflanzliches Material in dem Schaumnest Photo: H. Linke
Colisa lalia "RAINBOW": the male begins to bend around the female. Colisa lalia uses a lot of plant material for nest building

X40245-4 Colisa lalia "RAINBOW": bei Colisa-Arten sind die Eier leichter als Wasser. Oft sammeln die Eltern die Eier nicht mit dem Maul ein, sondern das Männchen stößt feine Luftbläschen durch die Kiemendeckel aus. Dadurch steigen die Eier praktisch von alleine ins Schaumnest auf. Photo: H. Linke
Colisa lalia "RAINBOW": in the genus Colisa, the eggs are lighter than water. Often the parents do not collect the eggs with the mouth, but the male exhales fine airbubbles through the operculum. This way, the eggs float into the nest by themselves.

 © Verlag A.C.S. GmbH

Photo: J. Vierke

A25467-4 Ctenopoma fasciolatum Form B: Bei den schaumnestbauenden Buschfischen sind die Weibchen kleiner als die Männchen. Zur Brutzeit zeigen sie ein helles Längsband.
Ctenopoma fasciolatum Form B: In the bubblenesting Bushfish, the females are smaller than the males. In brooding colouration they display a pale vertical bar.

Photo: F. Schäfer

A25517-4 Ctenopoma petherici: Bei den nicht brutpflegenden Buschfischen ist das Größenverhältnis der Geschlechter zueinander genau umgekehrt. Sie haben keine ausgesprochene Ablaichfärbung.
Ctenopoma petherici: In non-caring Bushfish the size proportions of the sexes is reversed. They do not display a special brooding colouration.

Photo: H. Linke

Photo: F. Schäfer

X58055-4 Macropodus concolor
Bei den Paradiesfischen strahlen die Männchen in dunklen
Prachtfarben während des Ablaichens. Im kleinen Bild: frischge-
schlüpfte Jungfische.

X58055-4 Macropodus concolor
In Paradise Fish the males show a dark display colouration. Small
photo: freshly hatched-out fry

© Verlag A.C.S. GmbH

X59005-4 Malpulutta kretseri: Das prächtige Männchen, erkenntlich an den lang ausgezogenen Flossen, umschlingt Photo: H. Linke
das Weibchen.
Malpulutta kretseri: The marvellous male (with very long fins) bends around the female.

X59005-4 Malpulutta kretseri: Das Weibchen erwacht vor dem Männchen aus der Paarungsstarre und sammelt die Eier Photo: H. Linke
von der Schwanzflosse des Männchens ab. Die Eier sind bei dieser Art schwerer als Wasser (Sinkeier).
Malpulutta kretseri: The female wakes up after mating and collects the eggs from the male´s caudal fin . The eggs in this species are heavier than water (sinking eggs).

X76280-4 Parosphromenus filamentosus: Die Prachtzwergguramis unterscheiden sich untereinander oft nur in der Brutfärbung. Der senkrechte Strich im Auge des Weibchens ist typisch für laichwillige Fische ("sexy eyes").
Photo: J. Schmidt

Parosphromenus filamentosus: The Licorice Gouramis can often be distinguished only by the brooding colouration. The horizontal bar in the female´s eye signals readiness for spawning ("sexy eyes").

X76460-4 Parosphromenus paludicola. Viele Parosphromenus-Arten verarbeiten nur noch ganz wenige Schaumblasen für ihr Nest. Diese Fische holen auch nur selten Luft an der Oberfläche.
Photo: J. Schmidt

Parosphromenus paludicola. Many Parosphromenus species use only few bubbles for nest building. These fish rarely breathe air.

Photo: J. Vierke

X82030-4 Pseudophromenus cupanus. Bei dieser kleinen Art kommt es zu einer unter den Labyrinthern einmaligen Umkehrung der Farbverteilung: Während der Paarung wird das Weibchen dunkel und das Männchen hell.
Pseudophromenus cupanus. In this small species the colouration of the sexes is reversed: during the mating, the female turns dark while the male turns light.

X82105-4 Pseudophromenus dayi. Der Rote Spitzschwanzmakropode bevorzugt im Aquarium Blumentöpfe als Laichhöhle Photo: U. Werner
Pseudophromenus dayi. The Red Spiketail prefers small claypots for spawning.

X93005-5 Trichogaster leerii. Die Schaumnester der Trichogaster-Arten sind oft sehr groß aber nicht sehr kompakt

Photo: H. Linke

Trichogaster leerii. The bubblenests of the Trichogaster species are often large but unstable

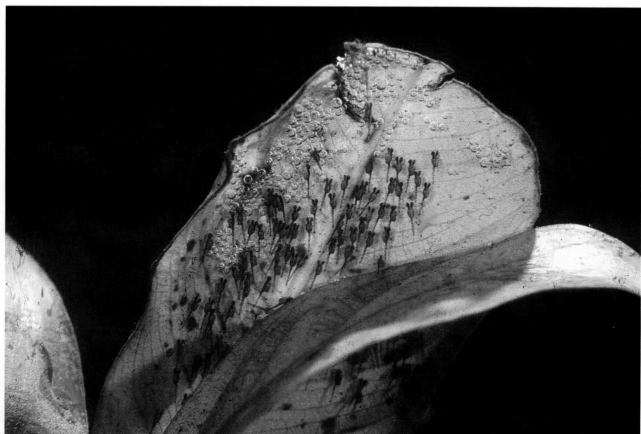

X94025   Die Larven von Trichopsis pumila heften sich mit speziellen Drüsen an der Unterseite des Blattes an, unter
dem sie geschlüpft sind.

Photo: H. Linke

*The larvae of Trichopsis pumila stick with the help of special glands to the undersurface of the leaf under which they
hatched out.*

© **Verlag A.C.S. GmbH**

X93045-4 Trichogaster microlepis. Auch bei den großen Trichogaster-Arten umschlingt das Männchen das Weibchen in typischer Labyrinther-Manier.

Photo: J. Vierke

Trichogaster microlepis. Also in the big Trichogaster species the male bends around the female in typical Labyrinth style.

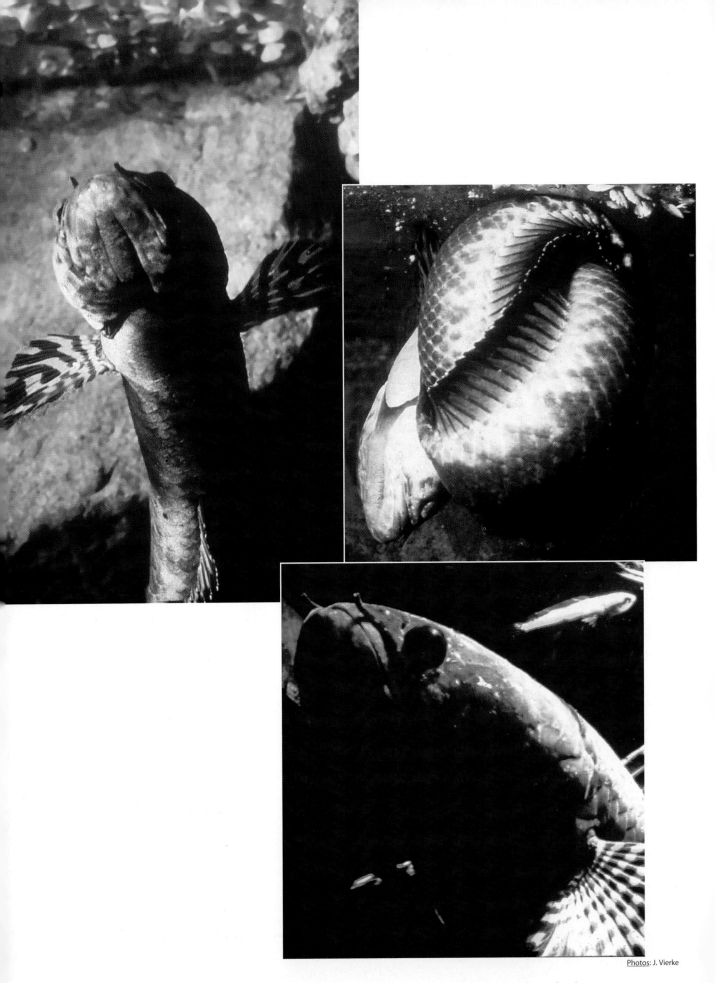

Photos: J. Vierke

X37205-4 Channa bleheri. Die Zucht der kleineren Schlangenkopffische erinnert in mancherlei Hinsicht an die der Labyrinther. Die Jungfische werden aber oft noch recht lange bewacht und geführt.
Channa bleheri.Raising smaller species of Snakeheads is quite similar to breeding Labyrinths. The young, though, are protected quite a long time.

© **Verlag A.C.S. GmbH**

Lieber Leser,

Sollten Sie im Besitz kleiner oder großer Dia- oder Foto-Sammlungen sein, bitte setzen Sie sich mit uns in Verbindung. Wir suchen für unsere nächsten Bücher immer gute Bilder von allen Fisch-Arten und besonders schönen Aquarien, und würden Ihre Bilder, natürlich gegen eine angemessene Benutzungsgebühr, gerne veröffentlichen.

To our readers,

if you are in possesion of either a small or large collection of slides or photographs please contact us. For upcoming books we are always on the lookout for good pictures of all types of fish and also for attractive aquariums. We would like to publish your photographs obviously for a suitable charge.

In jeder
Aqualog - *news*

internationale Zeitung für Aquarianer

erscheinen als **stickups** Ergänzungen
mit neuen Fischbildern, die Sie

hier

einkleben sollten, damit Sie immer "up-to-date" sind.

In every
Aqualog - *news*

international newspaper for aquarists

you will find **stickups** as supplements
which should be sticked in

here

to make sure that you are always up-to-date

Aqualog
im Internet
http:// www. aqualog. de

mit Informationen zu den Ergänzungen und
Neuerscheinungen

Aqualog
in the Internet
http:// www. aqualog. de

with informations about the supplements and
new puplications

In every
Aqualog - *news*

international newspaper for aquarists

you will find **stickups** as supplements
which should be sticked in

here

to make sure that you are always up-to-date

In every
Aqualog - *news*

international newspaper for aquarists

you will find **stickups** as supplements
which should be sticked in

here

to make sure that you are always up-to-date

Aqualog
im Internet
http:// www. aqualog. de

mit Informationen zu den Ergänzungen und
Neuerscheinungen

Aqualog
in the Internet
http:// www. aqualog. de

with informations about the supplements and
new puplications

In jeder
Aqualog - *news*
internationale Zeitung für Aquarianer
erscheinen als **stickups** Ergänzungen
mit neuen Fischbildern, die Sie

hier

einkleben sollten, damit Sie immer "up-to-date" sind.

In every
Aqualog - *news*
international newspaper for aquarists
you will find **stickups** as supplements
which should be sticked in

here

to make sure that you are always up-to-date

Aqualog
im Internet
http:// www. aqualog. de

mit Informationen zu den Ergänzungen und
Neuerscheinungen

Aqualog
in the Internet
http:// www. aqualog. de

with informations about the supplements and
new puplications

© Verlag A.C.S. GmbH

In jeder
Aqualog - *news*

internationale Zeitung für Aquarianer

erscheinen als **stickups** Ergänzungen
mit neuen Fischbildern, die Sie

hier

einkleben sollten, damit Sie immer "up-to-date" sind.

In every
Aqualog - *news*

international newspaper for aquarists

you will find **stickups** as supplements
which should be sticked in

here

to make sure that you are always up-to-date

Aqualog
im Internet
http:// www. aqualog. de

mit Informationen zu den Ergänzungen und
Neuerscheinungen

Aqualog
in the Internet
http:// www. aqualog. de

with informations about the supplements and
new puplications

In jeder
Aqualog - *news*

internationale Zeitung für Aquarianer

erscheinen als **stickups** Ergänzungen
mit neuen Fischbildern, die Sie

hier

einkleben sollten, damit Sie immer "up-to-date" sind.

In every
Aqualog - *news*

international newspaper for aquarists

you will find **stickups** as supplements
which should be sticked in

here

to make sure that you are always up-to-date

Aqualog
im Internet
http:// www. aqualog. de

mit Informationen zu den Ergänzungen und
Neuerscheinungen

Aqualog
in the Internet
http:// www. aqualog. de

with informations about the supplements and
new puplications

© Verlag A.C.S. GmbH

INDEX
Code - Numbers

INDEX
Code - Numbers

© Verlag A.C.S. GmbH

INDEX
Alphabet

INDEX
Alphabet

Italic Style: Common names

Literature Tips

Ein ausführliches Literaturverzeichnis für Labyrinthfische würde sich über mehrere, eng beschriebene Seiten ziehen. Wir verweisen an dieser Stelle daher nur auf allgemeine Schriften, in deren Anhang die meiste Primärliteratur gelistet ist.
It is impossible for us to give here a complete list of all literature on Anabantoids and related species; for this would need many pages. In the bibliography of the books listed here you can find further primary literature.

I. Books

Baensch, H. & R. Riehl (1992): Aquarien-Atlas 1. Melle
Baensch, H. & R. Riehl (1993): Aquarien-Atlas 2. Melle
Baensch, H. & R. Riehl (1994): Aquarien-Atlas 3. Melle
Baensch, H. & R. Riehl (1995): Aquarien-Atlas 4. Melle
Baensch, H. & R. Riehl (1997): Aquarien-Atlas 5. Melle
Britz, R. (1995): Zur phylogenetischen Systematik der Anabantoidei (Teleostei, Percomorpha) unter besonderer Berücksichtigung der Stellung des Genus Luciocephalus. Dissertation. Tübingen.
Linke, H. (1990): Labyrinthfische. Farbe im Aquarium. Melle.
Mayland, H.-J. (1980): Labyrinthfische. Artbeschreibung, Pflege, Zuchtverhalten. Minden.
Nieuwenhuizen, A. v. d. (1961): Labyrinthfische. Stuttgart.
Paepke, H.-J.(1994): Die Paradiesfische. Neue Brehm Bücherei. Magdeburg.
PISCES Publ. (Hrg.)(1995): Anabantoids. Tropical Fish Collection 5. Tokyo.
Richter, H.-J. (1979): Das Buch der Labyrinthfische. Melsungen.
Schmidt, J. (1996): Vergleichende Untersuchungen zum Fortpflanzungsverhalten der *Betta*-Arten (Belontiidae, Anabantoidei), Bibliothek Natur & Wissenschaft, Bd. 7, Solingen.
Vierke, J. (1986): Labyrinthfische. Arten - Haltung - Zucht. Stuttgart.
Vierke, J. (1978): Labyrinthfische und verwandte Arten. Wuppertal.
Vierke, J. (1993): Räuberbande im Aquarium. Stuttgart.

II. Magazines

Amigos del Acuario Publicacion de acuaristica para hispanohablantes
Akvariet Sweden
Aquafauna Belgium
Aqua Magazine Fair Wind Co., Ltd., Japan
Aquarama Strasbourg, France
Aquaria Suisse
Aquarium "aquarium" Primaris s.a.s., Italy
Aquarium fish magazine Fancy publications inc., Irvine, USA
Aquarium frontiers Aquarium frontiers inc., Brooklyn. N.Y., USA
Aquarium live Bede Verlag, Germany
Aquarium wereld Belgium
Aqua Plaisir Aqua Media, Villamblard, France
Aquaristik Aktuell Karl Heinz Dähne Verlag, Germany
Aquarium heute Aquadocumenta Verlag, Germany
Aquarium Magazine Strasbourg, France
Betta news Organ des Europäischen Anabantoid Club (EAC)
Das Aquarium Birgit Schmettkamp Verlag, Germany
DATZ Verlag Eugen Ulmer, Germany
Der Makropode Organ der Internationalen Gemeinschaft für Labyrinthfische (IGL)
Flair Organ des International Betta Congress (IBC)
Het Aquarium officieel orgaan van de Nederlandse Bond Aqua Terra, The Netherlands
Ichthyological Explorations of Freshwaters Verlag Dr. Friedrich Pfeil, Germany
Labyrinth Organ der Anabantoid Association of Great Britain (AAGB)
Practical Fishkeeping Tower Publishing Services, USA
T.F.H. Magazine T.F.H. Publications, Neptune City, USA
T.I. Magazin Tetra Verlag, Melle, Germany
VDA-Aktuell Organ der Verbandes Deutscher Aquarienvereine (VDA)

Viele der schönen Fische in diesem Buch konnten Ihnen nur vorgestellt werden, weil sich weltweit Idealisten zusammengeschlossen haben, um sich verstärkt diesen Arten zu widmen. Unterstützen sie diese Arbeit und werden Sie Mitglied in einer der folgenden Gemeinschaften:

Enthusiasts all over the world made it possible to show you so many of the wonderful species of Anabantoids in this book. Make shure that this fabulous work will keep on and help with your membership in one of the following associations.

AAGB
Anabantoid Assiciation of Great Britain

EAC
European Anabantoid Club

IBC
International Betta Congress

IGL
Internationale Gemeinschaft für Labyrinthfische
Comunita Internazionale per Anabantidi
Communaute Internationale pour les Labyrinthides CIL
International Anabantoids Association

Kontaktadressen finden Sie in den auf Seite 141 aufgeführten Magazinen
Contact addresses of these associations you will find in the magazines listed on page 141

Diese Liste erhebt keinen Anspruch auf Vollständigkeit / *This list may not be complete*

Supplement No.1 to
Loricariidae all I-Numbers
ISBN 3-931702-15-4

Supplement No.2 to
Loricariidae all I-Numbers
ISBN 3-931702-16-2

Supplement No.3 to
Loricariidae all I-Numbers
ISBN 3-931702-17-0

Supplement No.4 to
Loricariidae all I-Numbers
ISBN 3-931702-20-0

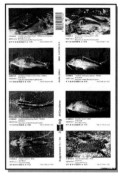

Supplement No.1 to
all Corydoras
ISBN 3-931702-18-9

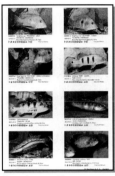

Supplement No.1 to
Southamerican Cichlids 1
ISBN 3-931702-19-2

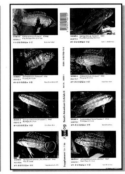

Supplement No.1 to
Southamerican Cichlids 2
ISBN 3-931702-12-X

Mit den aktuellen Ergänzungen sind Sie immer auf dem neuesten Stand !

With the actual supplements your books stay always up-to-date!

Wo bekomme ich diese schönen Fische ???

Der gute Zoofachhandel hat normalerweise einige dieser Arten vorrätig, oder kann sie besorgen, wenn Sie ihm genügend Zeit geben. Andernfalls wenden Sie sich an den Verlag, wir nennen Ihnen gerne Bezugsquellen in Ihrer Nähe.

Where can I get hold of these beautiful fish ???

Any reputable specialist pet shop should normally stock some of the species or be able to order them for you, if you give them sufficient time. Otherwise contact the publishers and we will gladly provide you with addresses in almost every country and city close to where you live.

Key to the
Symbols

fold out ➔

© Verlag A.C.S. GmbH